Be Your

Therapist

Find the

Cause And Cure

Body • Mind • Spirit

Patricia Hesnan

Oisin Publications
Oisin Centre of Natural Medicine
Killare, Ballinea, Mullingar, Co. Westmeath. Ireland
Telephone 044-56495

Website: www.healorcure.com
Email: info@healorcure.com.

First published June 2005

ISBN: 0-9550923-0-2

Pre-production: Topic Newspapers Limited, Mullingar, Co. Westmeath, Ireland.

Printed by: ColourBooks Limited, 105, Baldoyle Industrial Estate, Baldoyle, Dublin 13, Ireland.

Cover design, editing and layout: John Donohoe

Cover Photograph: Seamus Kelly.

Contents

These are some of the most common problems and issues people are experiencing in today's society

Are you feeling that your "get up and go" is gone? Do you feel tired and drained? It may be time to check and find the cause of your problem.

Do you feel you have lost control of your own destiny?

Do you feel there are times when you look beautiful on the outside but are crumbling apart on the inside?

Do you feel your life is out of control?

Do you live in the moment or are you exhausted, regretting the past, worrying about the future, while the present moment passes you by?

Do you feel a sense of panic today?

Are you peddling through life not knowing where you are at, or where you are going?

Do you feel you are moving too fast?

Have you been pushing yourself beyond your limits? Have you been pushing others beyond their limits?

Are you playing mind games with someone? Is there someone playing mind games with you?

Do you have difficulty forgiving yourself for some misdeed?

Are you battering away, criticising, condemning, rejecting, analysing, blaming and pushing yourself; believing it will help you on your spiritual journey?

Are you and your partner both dancing to the same tune or are *you* dancing alone on the dance floor of life?

Are you compatible with your partner?

Do you choose to believe that your behaviour has no bearing on what is happening around you?

Can you remember when you last felt connected to your partner?

Do you have a tendency to get involved in other people's problems?

You yourself are not wrong when the things you do, do not come up to your expectations or the expectations of others.

You can help your fellow men, but you are not responsible for anyone but yourself.

Acknowledgments

To the many people both here and in spirit I dedicate this book.

To the person who inspired and started me on my journey in writing, Solomon my guide, I thank you for your wisdom, direction, and stories without you there would be no stories and there would be no book. I thank my God, my spirit guides, angels, and Jesus for helping and guiding me in so many ways throughout my entire life.

To my husband John, my friend and soulmate. I thank him for the endless hours of support, love and encouragement. I thank him for his perseverance each and every time I was on the point of giving up. When I would travel one mile on this journey, he would travel five miles to encourage and help me. For the exhausting hours and days he spent editing and designing this book I thank him. Without him these stories would never have become a book.

To my children, Mandy, Fiona and David who have been such a joy and support to me, especially in times of sadness and loss. When life failed to have much meaning for me, and in times of darkness and despair, you were always there. You picked me up and encouraged me. You made my life worth living with your love and enthusiasm for life. You are three wonderful people, special gifts from heaven. I thank you.

To my mother, you have been there for me all through my years of ups and downs. Thank you for being there.

To my father, now in spirit, I thank you for your unending support, love and guidance.

To Donal, who risked his own life, by returning into a burning inferno to save my life and the lives of others. The greatest gift a man can offer his fellow man is the gift of life. I thank you Donal for the wonderful gift of life.

To Jacqueline Feely, my friend and colleague. I thank you for your encouragement and support, especially through some of the most difficult years of my life. Thank you for being there.

To those who helped and sometimes provided a much needed place of solace, for the writing of this book; especially Babs (now in spirit), Mary, Pat, Ruth and Simone. A special thanks to Ann Geoghegan and daughters Mary and Rose for the many years of help and support. To the many others who are part of my life. My sisters and brothers, Jean, Betty, Breda, Pat, Johnny, George, James, Gerrard, Ann, Rita and Gaybriel, and all their respective spouses and partners.

To the many friends I have met and who shared my journey of tears and laughter: Helen and Pat A. Vera and Charlie M. Helen and Jim O'H. Carmel (now in spirit). Cora (now in spirit) and Sean. Martina (now in spirit) and Ger H. Ann and Danny K. and family. Dermot (now in spirit). Johnny B. Kevin O'K.(now in spirit). Dolores O'K. Caroline N. John M. Moyra, and Mick. Barbara and Christy. Helen and Frank O. Robert O. Jimmy K. J.J. and Delia C. Sean F. Davey H. Maureen and Jimmy F. Alice H. Ben H. Joy J. Mick B. Mike and Ria N. Mary and Eamonn H. Maura and Terry F. Teresa and Tom T. Breda and Pat H. and family. To the many other people who have shared their journey with me, and allowed me to share my journey with them, in nursing, business and sport, I thank you.

A most special word of thanks to the many clients who have placed their trust in me and believed in me over many years. Without you, your experiences and your support, this book would not have been complete. You allowed me to be part of your journey of pain and tears, sadness and laughter, for all of this I will be eternally grateful. Thanks also to Darina W. Aine O'D. Mandy C. Anne H. Anthony F. Antonette T. Mary G. Ann L. Jody G. Majella M. Tommy K. and Emmy O' C. for their professional skills, comments, advice, and help in the production of this book.

Introduction

Life has a strange way of throwing us into unanticipated situations which can act as catalysts for profound change in our view of the world, our relationships and our place in the universe. One dramatic and shocking event can catapult us into a new world-view, where nothing around us ever appears the same again. Sometimes this transformation can happen in one brief moment and represent a quantum leap in terms of personal development. In others it can evolve a period of rapid change, of emerging – a chrysalis phase – during which the quality and characteristics of our personal relationships may fundamentally change forever.

Such a life-changing event occurred in my life in November 1989 when I found myself trapped in a blazing building and consequently had, what is generally known as a near-death experience. This was to trigger a period of intense transformation and growth in my life. I remember the paralysing feelings of fear and terror as the room in which I stood filled with smoke. I was fully aware of the fact that I was inhaling smoke and could feel my lungs expand and my body swell.

The voice of some distant nurse-tutor recited the textbook implications for the body of inhaling smoke; yet, I failed to observe what I knew to be a cardinal rule, of staying low where more oxygen would be available. Frozen by the terrifying realisation that the flames would soon engulf my body, I passed out of consciousness. I later woke up to find myself outside a burning building, in severe shock and suffering from smoke inhalation. The remainder of what happened prior to being hospitalised is mostly a haze.

When I was discharged from hospital, I returned to the home and family I had left a few days earlier and for the first time ever, – I truly saw. I walked around my house as if seeing it for the first time. I remember staring at a particular picture, which had been hanging on the same wall for the previous twenty years realising that I had never actually noticed it's details before.

House-bound by my injuries and poor health I would walk from room to room in awe of the smells, sounds and other details I had never truly registered before. It took a number of days for that intensity of consciousness to slip somewhat, but by that time I had gained valuable insight into my relationships, my conditioning, and the various issues in my life.

Over the months that followed I suffered from incredible nightmares. The psychic abilities, which I had as a young child had been reawakened, and I found their return overwhelming. In my dreams I began to have premonitions of future events. I understood that I was channeling and would go into deep trances, which could last for hours. I found this exhausting and sometimes frightening. However over time, I learned to communicate with my spirit guides. I have now learned to channel in a more controlled and comprehensive manner.

I see channeling as being like having a direct line of communication to the spirit world. If you consider this line of communication in terms of a pipeline, it is generally perceived that as children this pipeline is clear, but as we grow towards adulthood it becomes clogged with stones. The accident had somehow cleared my line to the spirit world in a very sudden and dramatic way.

Over the period, which followed the accident, I found my whole life turned up-side-down. I had spent years nursing full-time and running different businesses and a home. I had also been a very energetic sporty person. I now found myself in poor health and crippled by fear. I had worked in both general and psychiatric nursing so consequently turned to conventional medicine for help. I attended numerous doctors and went into therapy, but months later I was still at a point where I could not enter a building without first checking the fire-exits. I was claustrophobic and felt my life was controlled by fears.

Fortunately, I was eventually directed to a woman who had trained in a form of physio-emotional release therapy. This therapy served to not only relieve the intensity of my fears, but became my introduction to alternative therapies.

As I was discovering new worlds, my life was crashing around me. My marriage disintegrated and I lost both my business and my home. My struggle was difficult and over this period I had to deal with many of the underlying issues in my life. I started to explore the world of alternative medicines and therapies, and discovered a role for my psychic abilities and my experience in psychiatric nursing. Since that time I have worked and trained in many areas of alternative medicine. I trained in counseling skills, various forms of energy therapies and cranio-sacral realignment.

I have also learned a lot from my own personal life experiences, and this learning has given me a great capacity to empathise with the clients I meet, a capacity which I might not have maximised, had I not been caught in that fire accident.

At this point in my life I have reached a great peace. I live and work with my second husband, John at the Oisin Centre of Natural Medicine. Although painful, my journey of discovery has been exciting, invigorating and rewarding. In my work with clients, my concern is not just to address symptoms but also to seek out the cause, and through gaining an understanding of the underlying issue or cause, to help the client more effectively.

Having trained in a number of disciplines, I employ many different techniques, including allergy and environmental stress testing to get to the root of a client's problems.

During therapeutic energy sessions, my spirit guides help me by showing me images relating to past and present life experiences of the particular client. I am often shown past-life events as clearly as one might see them on a video. This event would have certain relevance for the client in their present life situation. The resonance of this event may still be affecting the client at a physical, mental or emotional level, and through counseling and physio-emotional release therapy, the intensity of the resonating emotion, e.g. anger, fear or sorrow, could be reduced or dissipated altogether. This allows the client to move forward in their life without the intensity of what might be a birth trauma, an early childhood experience or a past-life event limiting their capacity to live life fully.

Over the years I have dealt with countless clients who have presented me with a wide variety of symptoms and issues. I have been supported in my work by my spirit guides, particularly Solomon, who communicates his words of wisdom in the form of parable-like stories. I am often prompted during a therapy session to communicate one of these stories to a client and invariably some aspect of that story triggers a realisation in the client of an issue in their life. Clients find the visual images created by the stories increase the effectiveness of their therapy session.

Countless clients, upon leaving a therapy session ask me what to do next, what to read, where to get support and direction outside the therapy center. With this in mind and with the encouragement of my husband John, many clients, friends and colleagues in complimentary healing , I decided to write this book.

This book sets out to address itself to a wide range of people – those in therapy, those who may have finished therapy and even people who are independently seeking guidance on their journey through life.

There is many a crises on the way towards self-realisation.

This book aims to help the reader to focus on the issue, which is most relevant to them at this moment in time. The idea for this book was born out of the desire to allow clients to be individually directed by their spirit guides to the story most relevant and helpful to them at any particular time. The book can be read cover to cover like any conventional book. It can also be used in conjunction with the divination chart at the back of the book thus concentrating the reader's attention on one relevant chapter, story, or issue.

Each chapter/section of the book provides an opportunity to explore one issue of immediate relevance to the reader. Each issue is gently introduced and explored through imagery and story.

The book is written in an informal therapist to client style, avoiding any professional jargon or terminology. As the reader moves through the chapters, aspects of the stories gently center the reader within the issue. The reader, through spending time with the issue and answering a variety of questions, deepens their understanding of what is happening for them in their life.

In a loving and non-judgmental way the reader is led to an understanding of the cause, and where this issue originated, and is provided with guidance and direction as to how to proceed towards resolving that issue.

This not a book of do's and don'ts. It sets out to empower the reader to take control of his/her own life and so realise that at all times there is choice. They are encouraged to take responsibility for their own behaviour, stay aware of the affects of that behaviour on others, yet not live in other people's spaces.

Each chapter concludes with a list of positive affirmations from which the reader can choose one or more to carry with them through the day.

I have seen at first hand how the stories from this book have helped thousands of clients over many years, and I hope you find light and guidance in its pages.

Patricia Hesnan

– Real names and places have not been used in this book.

* "He" and "him" may be used in some stories, instead of he / her / they to simplify the explanations.

(1)
The Play

Do you feel you no longer have a space of your own?

Do you feel your time is no longer your own?

Do you feel you have been ousted from your favourite chair, your room, your garden or your home?

Have you been pushed aside by family, friends, relations or work colleagues?

Are there more and more people making demands on your space, your time and your money?

Have you forgotten what it is like to be master of your own destiny?

Have your forgotten where you are, who you are or where you fit in?

Are you wandering around aimlessly, not knowing where you are going?

Let us consider life in terms of a drama or a play and as we go through life each one of us builds our own individual theatre. We choose the players, write the script, set the stage, produce and direct. Players may come and go but it is still our own play. We make all the decisions, do all the hiring and firing and have the power to change the script, as we deem necessary or desirable.

Now consider what would happen if a person did not exercise that power and never changed the script. Naturally the various players would take it for granted that they were there to stay and that they no longer needed to make any effort to retain their parts.

To illustrate how this situation might unfold, you are invited to place yourself in the position of one person for whom this becomes reality. You may find some parallels between elements of this story and aspects of your own life.

Consider the theatre as the house you bought with your hard-earned money. You find yourself a partner/wife, who you think will play out a particular role supporting you. However instead of being of help, she decides not to take any responsibility for the part she accepted, regularly returning home late, overspending and always grumbling about the insignificance of her part. She says she would like to expand upon her role, so you both agree upon the new part of "*mother*" which she says will keep her occupied and give her more of a sense of purpose.

Consequently, an extra player "*baby*" is announced so the script is changed to accommodate his arrival, which is greeted with rapturous applause and tears of joy. He soon asserts his presence and makes his feelings known. He does not conform to the mealtimes, sleeping times, or the schedule, which you scripted. He has a schedule all of his own.

You asked for him and he arrived with a one-way ticket. He is on your stage and you must re-write the script all over again. You have accepted responsibility for him until he is old enough to write his own play, which will be based on a combination of what you teach him and his own learnings.

Your partner does not adapt as well as originally anticipated to the new role of "*mother*" so you both decide to hire another player "*childminder*" to look after the new arrival, so that your partner can get another job in another play. You have now introduced another player to your stage – the childminder.

As the years pass the number of players in your play continues to increase, but the stage has not changed. You feel the script has taken on a life of its own, and that nobody listens to you anymore. The other players seem to write in whatever parts suit them and write out the parts that do not.

You have now lost control over your play and regularly feel used and abused. Sometimes you assume the role of the night watchman, who lies awake at night wondering when and if your children will return home safely. Other times you are the cook who prepares meals to which nobody arrives on time, if they turn up at all. Seldom do *you* get a "lead role."

There are now many players playing different parts from different plays on one stage. It used to be your stage, but you got squeezed out over the years. You are unhappy with this situation. The most hurtful thing is that the other players do not seem to care or even notice anymore. Why should they? They may not have played their parts very well, but then you did not last very long at your part either, always changing and moving to allow more players in and thinking more players would solve your problems.

This begs one to question, your reasons for continuing to allow this unhappy situation to persist. Conditioning perhaps or maybe you have lost sight of your original character and forgotten the fact that you had the power to change the script to suit your character.

At this point, what can you do to help yourself to regain centre stage in your own play?

You cannot send the other players all packing – or can you? Are they too long established and set in their ways to make the necessary changes and move off your stage? This sounds like a complicated situation and a lot of trouble for all concerned, including you.

Pause for a moment and consider this dilemma. It is not as hopeless as it might seem. Remember you once wrote your own play, but in trying to accommodate everyone else, you allowed your own role to diminish. This is *your* play and only *you* can solve the problem.

Maybe you could write a new play, after all you wrote the first one. You can write it, play it, direct it and produce it all yourself if you want, but this time you may need to be more selective with the type of players you choose. You can create new boundaries for them and for yourself.

You can decide upon the extent to which you allow negativity to feature. Since you control the lighting, you can decide whether to highlight hope rather than hopelessness or to focus on joy rather than misery.

You can choose the aspects of your life to which you will give prominence. You can decide whether your theatre is filled with tears or laughter.

Your life is your very own play and you have the power to play it out whatever way you choose. Remember, that no matter how powerless you may feel, you are still the master of your own destiny.

This is *your* play and *you* have the power to

play it out *your* way.

Affirmation:

I am the person holding the pen and I start to write my new play today.

I will fill my play with joy and laughter.

I will play my part with a new awareness.

I will not hand over my part of my play to any one else.

I will choose the players with whom I will share my

stage.

It is *my* play.

It is *my* life.

I can play it *my* way.

(2)
The Dance Of Life

Are you feeling alone?

Are you feeling tired and dejected?

Are you feeling that you did all you could to dance in tune and keep the music playing?

You are in the dance hall of life.

The music may have stopped a long time ago. You may have been dancing on your own for a long time now. Your partner may have stopped dancing with you. They may have stopped listening to you and your music and left the dance floor a long, long time ago.

Maybe you need to retrace your steps and find out what went wrong in your dance of life. Some aspects of the dance may appear to be over e.g. relationships, marriage etc. Your partner may have left the dance floor. You may have sat down, feeling tired, dejected and alone. When you start to think about why you stopped dancing, you may start to blame. Blame the music. Blame your partner. Blame the venue.

- Do you ever stop and think back about how you were feeling as you were dancing?
- Can you remember the times you felt totally out of step with this person, i.e. opposite belief systems, opposite attitudes to life?
- Do you sometimes question if you ever really were in step with this person?
- Was it conditioning that brought you together? Conditioning says that at a certain age you should have a partner, or be married, have children, or have a home

of your own.

- Did you panic and accept the first person who asked you to share a dance with them?
- Was it low self-worth or low self-esteem that allowed you to continue dancing with this person even though you did not feel truly in step with them?
- What brought you together? Was it fear that no one else would want you that made you accept the first opportunity of a relationship? (Fear of being left on the shelf)?
- What held you together? Was it fear of loneliness? Was it conditioning? (What would the neighbours, friends, other family members say if you leave this relationship)?
- Sometimes a couple may stay together because of an unplanned pregnancy, or because of the possible affects that parting would have on the child, or children, or other family members.
- Were there times during your dance of life that you felt hurt, pain and exhaustion from trying to keep in step and come up to your own expectations and that of your partner?
- Was it fear of loneliness, that was controlling you and was a major factor in you continuing to dance with someone you knew you were incompatible with?
- As you danced were you held with tender loving care or were you kept at a distance?
- Did you hold your partner with tender loving care or did you keep them at a distance?
- Did you concentrate and focus on your partner and the dance you were dancing or were you preoccupied and distracted by other dancers (other people and their lives)?
- Did you have impossible expectations of your partner and their abilities?

- After a certain length of time had passed, did your partner have a standard of dancing (a standard of living and expectations) that was impossible for you to live up to?
- Did you have a standard of dancing (a standard of living and expectations) that your partner was unable to live up to?
- Was your partner distracted and not focused on you or the dance you both chose to share, after the first couple of dances (years)?
- Did your partner cease to make any effort to stay in step with you?
- Was dancing in time to the same music difficult for both of you right from the very beginning (no synchronicity from the start)?
- Did you both have difficulty hearing the music of life, and dancing to the tune of life (coping with and resolving life's issues and difficulties)?
- But most of all, did you experience and enjoy life's happy and joyous moments, or did they just pass you by, because you were so preoccupied in forcing yourself and your partner to dance to the same tune?
- Did you stop when you felt like stopping, or, did you wait for the music to stop? Did you wait for your partner to leave, or did you only realise the dance was over after you found yourself alone on the dance floor?

We sometimes dance to music we do not like. We may exhaust ourselves trying to change ourselves to suit the music and our partners. By the time the music stops, we may be too tired and worn out to dance to the music we do like. We may be exhausted and in too much pain to dance to any music. We may have lost interest in dancing with any other person, even someone who may be a more suitable dancing partner for us.

Your original partner may have lost the desire to keep in step with you a long time ago. The music may have stopped or slowed down, but you may have been so caught up in your conditioning, you did not even notice. Then one day, you realised you were standing alone on the dance floor. Your dancing partner and everyone else who was dancing around you had gone. Was it only then you got the feeling that you were on your own?

Do you now ask why someone did not tell you the music had stopped, but then, why should they? You were the one who wanted to keep dancing (living in denial). What do you do next? Start blaming of course. Blame everyone and everything.

Can you remember when the music slowed down or changed tempo (when there were changes in your relationship or marriage)? Your partner may not have been tuned in to you for quite some time. Can you even remember when it was, that they first left you standing (abandoned you) in the middle of the dance of life?

Maybe this dance was over for you a long time ago.

Blaming insinuates that your partner should have changed to suit *your* tune or that *they* did something wrong. Is it possible that you were never really in step with this partner?

Maybe you were both dancing to different tunes from the start.

Or maybe you were compromising yourself, going against the natural flow of life, your natural instincts and your gut feelings.

Did you continue to keep on dancing because of your conditioning?

Conditioning says, "Don't rock the boat, don't change." "What will the neighbours think?" "Don't tell anyone your problems, that would be admitting failure."

In blaming you are handing over your power to the other person to hurt, anger or annoy you. You may now need to learn to take responsibility for the part you played with your partner, in the dance of life. The dance with one particular partner may be over. It is what you have learned from this dance and this partner that is important.

If the dance is over with your present partner, what can you do now?

- First you need to discover the music you yourself would like to dance to.
- You need to learn what type of dancer you are.
- You can decide what type of partner you would like.
- You can decide what type of venue you would like.
- You can start a new dance to a new tune.
- You can also dance to a new tune with a more compatible partner.
- You can dance to a tune you both like.
- You can find a venue that is suitable to you both.

Affirmation:

I will dance to a tune that I enjoy.

I will find a more compatible dancing partner.

We will spend time choosing the music that enchants us.

We will stay in step with each other and dance to a wonderful tune in peace and harmony.

(3)
Expectations & Limitations

Expectations and Limitations is quite a broad topic.

We will illustrate here how you may lose sight of your own personal limits or the limitations of others consequently suffering serious repercussions.

Ask yourself the following questions.

Do you push yourself beyond your limits? Do you or have you had a problem recognising your limitations? Or, upon recognising them do you have a problem adhering to them? When you say "yes" or "no" do you allow others to change your mind? Do you leave it to someone else to decide when you have done enough work, exercise etc? Do you apply the learnings and experience of others, when you are creating limitations for yourself? Do you go beyond your limitations to the point, where you break down or are driven out of a relationship, marriage or job?

Are there times when you feel you have been pushed beyond your limits? Do you sometimes feel that this has been happening most of your life? Do your friends or family communicate expectations, which you find difficult to achieve? Do you ever feel that as soon as you have reached the top rung of the ladder, another rung automatically appears for you to climb?

So how do you recognise your limitations?

How do you take back your power, thus enabling you to decide when enough is really enough?

It is important to realise that failing to respect your own limitations may be a learned behaviour pattern. You may have been a child, when your natural ability to recognise your limitations were first taken away from you, but you can now learn to make the necessary changes when you feel and realise something is not good for you or your health, and that your hunch has validity. You may doubt your intuition at times but if you go with the feeling, then that is what is right for you. It is important to know your own limitations, likes and dislikes. How can someone else possibly know, recognise and respect them if you do not know them yourself? Your achievements in life are solely for *you*. *Your* learnings are unique and solely for *your* life's purpose.

Do you recognise and listen to your body's signals?

Our bodies have an intelligence of their own and if each of us could regain our childhood ability to listen to our bodies, we could avoid a lot of stress and illness. Do you take a break of your own free will, or does it take an accident or ill health to stop you and allow you to take stock of your life? How then do you judge how sick you really are? Does someone else tell you how sick you are, or do you act on how you really feel?

Very often this confusion begins when a child is very young. Maybe you had what are called tough parents, who did not believe in doctors or tablets, and when you complained of being sick, they may have seen this as an excuse to avoid doing chores, or that you were simply attention seeking. At the time you may have thought you were going to die from this sickness, but obviously your parents must have been right all along, or so you believed, – after all, you are still here. Perhaps you were just pretending. Is this what you now think? At the time *for you* it did seem to be a real pain and *you* felt really ill.

Do you know your limitations, or does someone else tell you when you have had enough alcohol, or do you wait until the barperson tells you that you have had enough or do you wait until you are out of control on all levels? Do you wait until your brain, liver and stomach etc., are damaged beyond repair before you begin to realise when enough is enough?

If you learned to "tune out" from your body's pain level at a young age, you may have difficulty "tuning in" at a later stage. When you eat, do you know your limitations? Do you eat what you feel like eating or do you eat the food others recommend you should eat even if it makes you feel unwell? When you were young your natural instincts were telling you what foods agreed and did not agree with your system. Did your parents listen when you said, "I don't like onions?" You may have been told to eat them, despite the stomach cramps they gave you, – because your parents believed they were good for you. So you may have learned at an early age, to eat what someone else thought was good for you, and not what *you* instinctively felt agreed with your particular system.

Your body instinctively knows when it cannot tolerate a particular food. When allergists discover a child has sensitivities to certain foods, the parents often remark that as a baby that child did not like the foods in question.

At the outset it was acknowledged that "Limitations and Expectations" is quite a broad topic. Let us now "flip the coin" and address the issue of the expectations we project onto others. It is important to pose the following question:

As parents do we push our children beyond their limits to a point where they cannot cope?

There are many different ways in which we may push our children beyond their limits. Sometimes we may buy toys and books for them, beyond their intellectual capabilities. This may be in order to advance them further and faster. Where a particular sport may have been merely a fun pastime for a child, parents and teachers may push the child to become competitive. We may buy our children a piano or a guitar or perhaps the best pair of football boots available, not so that they can enjoy them, but more often so that they can achieve more with them.

Similarly, parents may make comments such as, "See Tom next door, look at how well he did in his exams." "How about Cousin Billy, he got on the soccer team, how come you were not picked for the team?" "You could be learning or doing something useful, instead of sitting around talking to your pals or riding around on that bicycle all day."

Some parents no matter how high a standard their child achieves, may still give out the message that "it is good – but they could do better." With constant pressure and the continuous struggle to achieve the standards expected by the parents, a sense of hopelessness and helplessness may set in at an early age.

Young people sometimes find it difficult to differentiate between all the pressures in their lives i.e. teachers, parents, peer or self-induced. They may try in various ways to communicate that it is all too much and that they can no longer cope. Some do this by withdrawing completely into themselves. Others may turn to drink or drugs to relieve the pressure. Unfortunately there are also those who, in an effort to draw attention to their dilemma, may take their own lives whether by accident or design.

If you can relate to any of these stories, the following questions may be of help. If the answer to some of the following questions is "yes" it may be time to look at your life and your way of being.

Taking Stock of your life:

The questions are posed to help you take stock of your life and help you to move forward in a positive way.

- Are you struggling in your effort to make your relationship work?
- Are you trying to force your partner into making your relationship work?
- Do you feel angry and resentful towards those who pushed you and had expectations of you beyond your capabilities?
- Do you feel anger towards yourself for not recognising your own limitations?
- Do you feel you have wasted many years "people pleasing" and never really listening to or being aware of your own needs?

- Do you recognise your own limitations and the limitations of others?
- Do you have a problem saying "no" to yourself and to others?
- Are you overloading your physical, emotional and mental bodies and not recognising their limitations and capabilities?
- Are you exhausted and in ill health with all the pressure you have placed upon yourself?
- Are you exhausted and in ill health, trying to push others beyond their limitations?

You may have been a child when you learned or believed you had no choices, but you are now an adult who can become aware of the choices you do have, and the choices you can make for your own benefit and the greater good of all.

How does your body know now that it has a choice? How do you learn how to regain your natural ability to tune into your body?

Firstly by listening to your body and acting on what your body is saying to you. By not following someone else's belief system of what *they* may think is good or bad for you. By tuning into *how you feel.* By getting in touch with your intuition and gut feelings and acting on what they are saying to you.

You *can* make changes. Your past will have affected you, but try not to allow it to control you. It does not have to. Where you may have regrets, do not be afraid to acknowledge them. Be kind to yourself and remember whatever you may have done or not done, you worked with the awareness you had at that particular time.

Sit down and take a deep breath and as you exhale ask yourself:

- How do you feel at this moment in time?

- Are you feeling tired? Are you feeling lonely? Are you feeling sad etc? Give yourself permission to have this feeling. Getting in touch with your feelings is what is important. It may not be convenient for you to act on these feelings at this moment in time, but knowing you have the choice is what makes the difference.
- Do you know you can set limits for yourself? You may need help to do this.

At all times you have free will. Whether you exercise this free will or not is also your choice.

Affirmation:
I will not push myself beyond my limitations.

I will not allow others to push me beyond my limitations.

I will not push others beyond their limitations.

God help me to see my limitations.

God help me to know my limitations.

God help me to create my limitations.

Nora's Story:

Nora was the second eldest of ten children. She was a very sensitive child who always tried to please her parents. Nora lived in a home where there were regular rows and arguments, particularly regarding the delegation of responsibility for chores about the house. At a very young age Nora proved herself a capable and dependable child. Consequently her parents assigned her the most difficult chores. They seldom spoke words of praise, thanks or appreciation and at times took her completely for granted. Since her parents never questioned her limitations, Nora never did so either. Whether sick or well Nora did everything she was asked, never recognising when enough was enough.

In her anxiety to please she lost track of her own body's

limitations. She not only pushed herself beyond her endurance level, but also created the impression to everybody that she could do just about anything, without ever getting tired or sick.

Years later in a therapy session Nora remembered having teeth extracted when she was about nine years old. Nora was still bleeding considerably when she arrived home, so her mother suggested that she should lie down for a while. When her father returned from work and discovered that Nora was resting, he became very angry and ordered Nora out to the garden to weed the vegetables. She explained to her father that she just had some teeth extracted and was feeling weak and dizzy. Her father reacted angrily saying, "A little thing like having a few teeth removed should not stop someone like you." Feeling hurt and unheard Nora attempted to follow her father's orders but collapsed. Her body rejected being pushed beyond its limit.

Alas this incident was but one of many which started Nora off on a lifetime of not recognising her own limitations. She had a tendency to push herself beyond her limits in all aspects of her life, work, sport, food and drink. She would ignore her own pain, exhaustion or discomfort in her effort to oblige others. Some years later, Nora married and had children. Even when Nora did complain, her husband and children did not pay a lot of heed to her, because in spite of her complaints, she always seemed able to continue with her normal work and routines.

Sadly Nora suffered severe consequences as a result of ignoring her body's signals, one such instance being when Nora then in her thirties, suffered a back injury. The doctor advised her that unless she took complete rest, a full recovery would be unlikely. Her husband, who was with her during the doctors visit, later declared that he did not consider her to be as bad as the doctor was indicating.

In her effort to please and accommodate others, Nora chose to disregard both the doctor's advice and the pain she was suffering and resumed her usual household duties. She did however take the prescribed painkillers. Unfortunately since they blocked her pain, which would naturally have indicated to her that she was injuring herself, Nora unintentionally inflicted additional damage to her back, damage which became patently obvious when the affects of the painkillers had worn off. The result of ignoring her own body's signals and the doctor's advice was that she suffered with chronic back pain and spent years on painkillers and anti-inflammatory drugs.

Another significant incident, which eventually resulted in Nora attending for therapy, happened shortly after Nora had suffered a miscarriage. Her husband suggested that they go for a walk together. She convinced herself that, "If he thinks I can go for a walk, then I must be able to," and so they set off. However she soon began to feel weak and knew she could not continue walking. She tried to persist, but in her pain and frustration started to cry. When her shocked husband asked why she was crying, Nora replied that she was too weak to walk any further. Her husband dismissed this saying, "Of course you can." Nora's crying intensified and she shouted at him in a way she had never done before. "Do you not hear me, I am not able to walk any further?" She cried uncontrollably. All the old memories came rushing back again. Her father had not heard her and now her husband did not hear her. Most significantly of all she realised that she never listened to or heard herself. She had failed to pay attention to the voice within, which warned her when she was pushing herself beyond her limits.

Nora did not value her own limitations. Her biggest problem was that she could not compromise. Everything had to be done to extremes. Nora had to learn that if she felt pain, only *she* knew and felt how bad it was. Only *she* knew when to stop and pay attention to the pain.

Nora could now see the pattern in her life and where it had all started. She could see how she had created the impression to everyone around her that "the sky was the limit" as far as what she could do was concerned.

Nora now realises only she can decide what her own limitations are. She must also decide when and how, she must act on them. Most importantly, Nora realises she must stop and slow down when her body gives her the signals to do so. If she does not act on her feelings, how then can she expect others to do so?

It has taken a lot of pain, both physical and emotional, for Nora to take notice of her feelings, know her limitations and consider how she portrays them to others. With professional help, good friends and a more understanding and balanced relationship, Nora has learned how to create her own limitations, and is now leading a happier and healthier lifestyle.

(4)
The Bucket

The bucket is what holds your life's resources. It is also you.

Are you feeling that your "get up and go" is gone? And if not gone completely, you may be feeling that it is being depleted in some way. You may not know the cause or the reason why. You may have some queries about your overall health and general well-being. You may need help and guidance to check this out.

If you can find the cause, you are halfway to the cure.

If you took a bucket of water on a journey and never checked to see if the bucket was empty or full, you could be in for a bit of a shock. You may assume you will have water until your journeys end. However, at some stage of the journey, you may have noticed that your bucket did feel a bit lighter, but you may have been too busy to check and see what was causing the problem.

How many of us have almost completed our journey without taking time out to check our bucket (our supply of life's resources)? Have you been drained and exhausted by traumas in your life? Have you pushed yourself beyond your limits in many aspects of your life? We sometimes look back and realise without being aware of it at the time, that the water in our bucket (our life's resources) was draining away slowly but surely.

Is your bucket full, half full, or empty?

- Do you remember the last time you looked into your bucket?
- When you last looked into your bucket and found it was

nearly empty, did you ask why?

- Is it possible someone was stealing your water when you were not looking?
- Were there people in your life taking things from you without asking; your possessions, your time or your money?
- What is left for you?
- Is what you have left in your bucket enough to sustain you for the remaining part of your journey through life?
- Maybe it is you who is spilling the water.
- Maybe you have been giving away your water indiscriminately (giving away your time, energy, possessions or money etc).
- Maybe you are moving too fast on your path, running all over the place and not looking where you are going.
- Maybe there is a leak in your bucket. Perhaps you are continually attempting to fill this bucket, never questioning why it is emptying so fast.
- Maybe you are unable to hold on to the necessities of life. Do most things filter through your fingers, friends, jobs, relationships and money?
- Do these only last you for short periods of time?

When you discover what is causing your problem, what do you do? Do you change direction? Do you opt for the quick fix easy way out i.e. alcohol, drugs etc., when dealing with life's issues? Or do you wander through life spending a lot of your time socialising and wandering from place to place not knowing where you are going, or where you have been most of the time?

You may need to make some changes now.

There may still be holes in your bucket. Your family and friends may have long since gone. Your bucket, (your ability to contain life's resources) may not hold water. You may feel too old, tired or worn out to start off with a new bucket or repair the damage you have done, so you may have to depend on someone else's supply of water. If this is so you may have to rely on whatever someone else e.g. family, friends etc., can do for you or supply you with.

If you did not learn how to fix your bucket (if you did not learn how to take care of yourself or take responsibility for yourself) – you may have to rely on others to sustain you and share their resources with you when and how they please or see fit.

What happens when you discover half way along your journey that you are spilling your own life's resources, living it up, late nights, partying, overspending and so on? Do you decide to stop or slow down and take time out to see what is happening for you?

Ask yourself why you were moving so fast?

What was driving you?

- Was it fear?
- Was it conditioning?
- Was it habit?

You *can* slow down but only *you* can decide how and when. If you do not notice how much water you are losing from your bucket, you may not see the necessity for stopping and checking your supply until it is almost too late. (Your health, finance, marriage, relationships, job or business may be practically drained dry before you notice that you are running low on your supply of life's resources).

What happens if you have not looked into your bucket at all? You may have taken it for granted that this bucket of water would last forever, but waken up one day and find it completely empty.

- Can you remember when the bucket started to get lighter?

- Can you remember where the source of water came from in the first place?
- Do you even know where to start looking for more water?
- Are you now too thirsty and tired to even walk?
- Are you so worn out taking care of everything and everyone around you, that you do not now have the energy to take care of yourself?
- Do you even know where to start looking for answers to your problems?

On the other hand you may be a person who has always kept your bucket topped up (full of life's resources i.e. good food, exercise, joy and laughter, loving and caring for yourself with plenty to share around).

Stop today, this minute, take a good long look at your bucket (your life) and ask yourself:

What sort of condition is your bucket in today?

- Is it strong?
- Is it weak?
- Is it full of holes?

Do you have enough water left in your bucket for the remainder of your journey?

- Our life is like the bucket.
- Our body is like the bucket.
- The source comes from within, not without.
- It is never too late to begin again.
- Where there is life there is hope.

Affirmation:

Today I will check my bucket.

Today I will check my life's resources.

If my life's resources are draining away, I will stop the behaviour that is allowing this to happen.

Through insight and awareness I will stop the cause.

(5)
Compatibility

Do you feel compatible in your relationship or do you have doubts as to whether you are compatible with your partner or not?

Compatibility in this context is the blending together of two energies (two people) on different levels.

Some people may be compatible or connect on one level only.

Some may find they connect at many more levels.

Some may not connect or be compatible on any level.

There are a number of levels of compatibility when it comes to two people in a relationship, physical, emotional, mental and spiritual.

Physical:

They may both be attracted to each other physically. When they meet it could be love at first sight and both parties may enjoy a very healthy physical relationship, but not necessarily be compatible on other levels.

Emotional:

A couple could be emotionally compatible, i.e. relating and responding to each other emotionally. Responding in similar ways to emotional situations. They may relate on this level only.

Mental:

As a couple they may not necessarily engage in a physical relationship quite as much as they will engage in a mental relationship, by this we mean more of a "blending of the minds" when it comes to belief systems and attitudes. They may enjoy lengthy conversations and discussions.

Spiritual:

A couple may be said to be compatible because they have similar views on spirituality. They may have had past lives together and now blend with each other as far as attitudes towards God, and spiritual beliefs are concerned.

It may take many years for partners to realise the incompatibility in their relationship. They may need to ask themselves at what levels they were compatible initially if any, and whether there are sufficient grounds for a relationship. You and only you can decide.

A break-up of a relationship:

A break-up may be inevitable. Outside influences or a third party may be a factor in the break-up of a relationship, but they are not necessarily the cause of a relationship breaking up. It is only one or the other or both of the two people, who have made the connection in the first instance, who can decide, if, when, and how, to break this connection.

Ask yourself:

- At what level was the connection made at the beginning of the relationship?
- What are the levels of compatibility in this relationship now?
- How strong are these connections?
- Do you have any doubts about the compatibility in your relationship?
- Do you feel connected to your partner at this moment in time?
- Have you or your partner made changes in your individual lives, since you first chose to make a commitment to each other?

One or the other of you, may have chosen to go on a spiritual journey, whilst the other may have decided that they were comfortable to remain where they were at. No one has a right to judge you or decide which is the right road for you to take.

Like the stories of "The House" and " The Shoes" it may now be time to look at your relationship.

What part are you playing in this relationship, if any?

- Is this relationship nurturing for you, body, mind and spirit?
- Are you and your partner in step with each other, or do you feel the dance is over for you? If the answer to this is yes, read the story on "The Dance."
- Are you or your partner game playing? If the answer to this is yes, read the story on "The Game of Life."
- Are you or your partner attempting to control each other? If the answer to this is yes, read the story on "Control."
- Are you enabling each other rather than helping? If the answer to this is yes, read the story on "Enabling."
- Do you respect each other's boundaries? If the answer to this is no, read up on "Boundaries."
- Is conditioning holding you together? If the answer to this is yes read "The Bird in the Cage."
- Are you trying to take responsibility for what is not yours? If the answer to this is yes, read the story "The Hub of the Wheel."
- Do you minimise what is happening for your partner? If the answer to this is yes, read the story on "Minimising".
- Are the expectations in this relationship too high for both of you? If the answer to this is yes, read the story on "Limitations and Expectations."
- Are you trying to make this relationship work regardless

of the signs that it may be over for both of you at this point in time, not necessarily forever, but maybe for the moment? If the answer to this is yes, read the story "The Toy."

- Do you remember when you last connected with your partner if at all?

Allow yourself time to answer these questions honestly. Try not to blame yourself or your partner. In blaming you become powerless. Allow the feeling rather than the blame.

Guilt:

You may have feelings of guilt when a relationship comes to an end, also self-blame, especially when you see the affects this break-up has had on family and friends. You are responsible for what you have said and done, but not for the other person's reaction to it.

Their reaction is based on their past and how past behaviours and reactions have helped them to cope and survive. Guilt is a very controlling emotion. Try and acknowledge your own feelings of guilt if there are any, by saying, "It is the best I could do at the time."

It is the best you could do with the circumstances you were in, and with the knowledge you had at that particular point in time. It is not necessarily what you would do with the awareness and knowledge you have now. You are still responsible for any part you play in the break-up of the relationship.

A third party may appear on the scene and make a connection with one of these partners at a different level. This can upset the relationship, but this is neither right nor wrong, for one person or the other.

The learning experience with the first partner may now be complete, and a time for a learning experience with a second partner and maybe even a third, may be ready to begin.

As long as a learning is being experienced with a partner

at one or more levels, it may be necessary to remain in that relationship, (connection) until the learning is complete. If the learning is not complete, one or other of the partners may continue to return to the other, over and over again in this lifetime. They may also have gone through this process in many other lifetimes.

Many of us resume relationships that were incomplete in previous lifetimes. The completion of the learning may not necessarily involve a long-term relationship. It is important to be aware that when we have outgrown a relationship, the time may have come for us to move on and to also allow the other partner to move on.

There may be times when you may believe that only you can fulfil a need for someone else or you may believe, a certain person can be the only person who can fulfil your needs and wishes. However, your feelings may be telling you to "let go" of this person. It is not your responsibility to try and meet someone else's needs, or for someone else to try to meet your needs or wishes.

There may be times when you feel the learnings with your present partner difficult and painful. However, if you move from this partner to a new partner before your learning is complete, you may find yourself returning to him/her again and again, in an effort to complete your learning. It may take you many more lifetimes before meeting this person again, and reconnecting where the previous connection was broken off. This may be necessary, so that you may both continue together once more on your ultimate path of learning.

If you are going through one learning experience, then this is all you have to deal with at this moment in time. When energies like the positive forces i.e. God, the universe, guides, help to unite two people to experience a learning, no man has the right to try to force them apart, or force them to stay together, after their learning is complete.

You both may need professional help for this relationship to survive. You may also need professional help to allow both of you to go on your separate journeys.

No one person is wrong or right when a relationship does not work out. The learning for both of you may be complete for now. Sometimes it is necessary for a couple to part from each other, so that one or both can gain more from life's teachings and experiences. This may enable you to be more compatible with each other at a later date, or indeed compatible with a new partner.

No one should be kept in jail a moment after their sentence (their learning in this life) has been served, and no one should be allowed out one moment too soon.

If a person escapes and never completes his sentence, he will always be on the run. He will never know where, or when, he might be captured and imprisoned again. It could be years or it could be many lifetimes – but it will happen.

That which is not joined cannot be broken.

That which is only partially joined, can easily be broken.

- Now, light a candle for yourself.
- Be gentle and patient with yourself.
- Reward yourself for having the courage to take the time to look at your relationship.
- Spend a little time each day meditating.
- Create some quality time for yourself, you deserve the best life has to offer.
- The meeting of like-minded souls is like the beginning of a new cycle in life.

Affirmation:

I know I can be compatible with another person.

I know there is someone who will be compatible

with me.

I know my soul mate is out there awaiting the day, when we shall meet again on our ultimate path of learning.

I will be patient whilst awaiting the meeting of my soul mate.

(6)
The Race

Are there any aspects of this story that you can relate to?

This story of Sean could be relevant to so many of us in life.

A case history:

Sean was a successful businessman. He had a hectic lifestyle wheeling and dealing, working, partying and socialising. He drove fast sports cars, hooting slow drivers off the roads. He did not have much regard for animals or birds that crossed his path of speed.

When he did not get a fast response from business acquaintances, he became very angry. He had very little patience, with either young or old. He was in a dreadful hurry to "get on" with his life. In his haste he did not have much time for friends, family or work colleagues.

Sean had all the trappings of success, a big house, nice clothes, a fast car and a successful business. At one stage he felt he had achieved his life's ambitions, but now believes he is at a crossroads and feels there is something missing in his life. He attends for therapy complaining mostly of feeling stressed out and unhappy. He is also anxious to find out what purpose and meaning life holds for him now.

The therapist asked Sean's guides for some guidance.

Sean was shown a scene from (his life) the race that he had just run. The guide asked him to turn around, and look at the scenes of destruction he had left behind. The people he had knocked down and walked upon. Those he had passed by who needed help. Those who had asked for support along the way but being too intent on getting to the finishing line himself, Sean failed to hear their cries for help.

Sean's guide said to him, "What is the meaning of all those rows of empty alcohol bottles? Look back at your race-track and explain why so many are lying injured. Some were running slower, but got injured as you ran over them. Some wanted to run faster but you would not let them pass. Some only asked what type of shoes you wore, but you would not tell them. Some asked for a drink of water, you had plenty but you would not share it. Some just wanted to ask a question, but you had no time to talk to them, because you were in so much of a hurry to finish this race and get it over with. Now, look back at your life and the carnage you have left behind in this race and tell us what we should do about it?"

Needless to say Sean was devastated by all of this, for he had believed all his life that it was all about succeeding, achieving and getting to the top that mattered. Sean always believed that you should live life as fast as you can, fitting in as much as you can, wheeling and dealing. The ultimate aim, Sean believed, was to achieve status symbols and become a millionaire, he could then settle down and live his life in peace, with the money and security he had accumulated throughout a lifetime of hard work. In fact, now that he had almost reached this position, he felt he was in a void, with no more challenges and no further purpose.

His guide told him, that he had missed out on some of the most important things in life, awareness, empathy, truthfulness, patience, tolerance, honesty, compassion etc. He also advised him, not to rush through each day, wondering when real life is going to begin. "Each and every second, minute, hour, day, month and year is your real life. Every minute act or deed each moment of that time – is your life. You are living your real life now, – this very second."

"You cannot change the past, but if you learn from it, it then becomes positive. The past is history. The future is only speculation. There is only the moment you are in right now."

"You ask us a question and we give you an answer, now you have become more aware with this new knowledge. Learn from it and start a different race. Start now – today – this moment."

"A new race starts every moment of every day for everybody."

"It is not winning the race or getting to the finishing line that is important but what kind of race you run. With each piece of knowledge, there is a new level of understanding and an expanded level of awareness."

Sean now starts his new race with great deliberation.

- He takes care not to push or hold back his fellow runners.
- He keeps a close eye on anyone who needs help, though not taking their issues on board or taking responsibility for them.
- This time he is moving more slowly, he knows now there is no time limit on this race.
- He understands now, that it is how he runs this race (how he lives his life) that is important – not how fast.
- It is the quality of his life and not the quantity of his achievements that is important.

The guides say that life is like a race.

We start our race on earth the day we are born. There are many people in this race, parents, family, friends, relations, acquaintances, work colleagues etc. Some we get to know well and share our experiences with. Others we meet only briefly. There are others in this race whom we may never meet, but we are all still in the same race.

At the end of the day, what is most important is how we interact with each other, the quality of our life and how we live each and every moment. In the end, the race of life (our life) is about unconditional love. Learning to love and respect our fellow human beings and ourselves.

Life is not about what we do, it is about how we do it.

Light a candle, sit down, take a deep breath and ask yourself,

What sort of race am I really running?

Is it a fair race?

Am I helping all the other runners along the path they are on?

What am I learning on my journey?

"It is better to walk one mile and see everything, than to run ten miles and see nothing."

(7)
Denial

Where there is denial there can be no learnings.

A person in denial chooses to believe, that their behaviour has no bearing on the issues that surround them. They can convince themselves, that their behaviour is not responsible for the problems regarding their physical, emotional or mental health. They may convince themselves, that their behaviour is not responsible for their financial problems. They may deny all responsibility for how their behaviour has affected or is affecting other people's lives. They can minimise the affect their behaviour is having on others by saying "It's no big deal." "You're exaggerating." "You're making it up."

The person in denial may have many health problems, from over indulgence to addictive or dysfunctional behaviour. He can seriously injure himself and others, by crashing vehicles and engaging in aggressive behaviour. This can also cause financial hardship to himself, his family and friends. The person in denial can convince himself and others, that he does not drink much, "I only had a few." His behaviour makes a different statement. This person may find every excuse for their dysfunctional behaviour, when confronted. People in denial are convinced, despite all the obvious signs, that the entire story was made up to get at them.

"It was not me."

"You must have spent the money."

"The bank made a mistake."

"Someone annoyed me."

"You drove me to it."

"Someone must have put something in my drink."

"I did not eat all day."

"I never said that."

The crashed car is once again repaired. The empty bottles discarded, the dirty carpet cleaned. The broken door and window repaired. The clean up is usually carried out by someone else in the family or by a friend, but not, by the person in denial.

The person in denial does not take responsibility for his behaviour or the consequences of his behaviour. He can deny and truly convince himself that he was not even present, on the days that those events took place, let alone have participated in them.

The person in denial may attend a health care professional for persistent health problems. He may be suffering from coughs, lung problems and chest pains, yet when asked if he was a smoker, he may reply:

" Just an odd one here and there."

" I only smoke Ops (other peoples)."

" Only when I'm drinking."

This is despite the fact that he has hundreds of pounds less in his pocket each year and his home and car are littered with cigarette ends.

The person in denial with health and food related problems i.e. digestive problems, weight problems, lung and heart problems, and sometimes many more, when asked what their diet and eating habits are like they can sometimes reply, "I don't really eat or drink that much".

This is despite the fact that they may be continually eating and drinking throughout the entire day. These may not be large amounts of food, but they may binge to excess on snacks and fizzy drinks on a regular basis. A considerable amount of the food which this person takes into their body may be neither healthy or agreeable with their particular system.

They may take digestive aids and pain-killers to combat the harmful affects of certain foods and drinks on their bodies. They may regularly find themselves attending healthcare professionals for solutions to their problems. When approached by family and friends who may be concerned about them and their state of health, they may go through numerous health-checks, and take up a strenuous exercise and fitness programme. Their health or weight related problems may not change, because they have not changed the cause of their problems i.e. over-indulgence in certain foods and drinks.

At this point, the person in denial may resort to blaming others for their problems i.e. "It's hereditary, all the family have the same problems, it's what they are putting in the foods these days." (Nothing at all to do with the quality or quantity of food this person is eating.) "My food is prepared for me, what can I do but eat it." "I'm all the time on the road, I don't have time to eat properly, I don't have time to cook for myself, snacks and take-aways are handy for people like me."

This person may be in denial that his own behaviour contributes in any way to his health or diet related problems. He cannot see, or does not wish to see, or take any responsibility for the behaviour that is affecting or damaging his health.

The businessman in denial will continue to spend and live lavishly and maintain his usual standard of living, wining, dining and gambling, despite the depleting state of his bank accounts, and despite the warnings from his financial advisors that his business is in jeopardy. He gets all the warnings, sees all the signs, but convinces himself that it's not really happening.

He can continue like this until he loses everything but will still convince himself that none of this is his fault. His reasoning may be:

"My suppliers were unreliable."

"My staff were not up to the job."

"My accountant was ripping me off."

The person in denial may instantly deny having said cruel words or carried out hurtful actions. This may be in order to save himself, from the possible consequences of what he has done, and from fear of how other people may react. When he instigates an argument and is unable to deal with the repercussions, he will blame someone else for starting it and for the outcome. Meanwhile the other person is hurt and angry, not because of what he has said or done, but because of his denial of what he has said or done.

Persons in denial who have engaged in either physical, emotional, mental or sexual abuse, can, despite evidence to the contrary, convince themselves and others that they were in no way responsible for such acts. If the person in denial is confronted and forced to admit having engaged in abuse of any kind, they often minimise and deny the devastating affects of their behaviour by saying, "They drove me to it". "I didn't think it was any harm." "I was drunk when it happened." "The person who is saying, I abused them, is lying or making it up to get at me." "I can't remember." Meanwhile the abused person may be attending for therapy and trying to heal from the trauma, which they have experienced.

Where there has been abuse of any kind it is more difficult for the abused to find closure and heal from the events whilst the abuser remains in denial.

The person in denial can convince himself, that the problems within his family and other people around him have nothing to do with him. He may blame a nagging partner, financial pressure and health issues as the problem and the cause of his behaviour. He sees his distressed children. He sees his wife/partner spending most of her days and nights in tears. He sees his friends avoiding him and wanting less and less to do with him. He convinces himself this has nothing to do with him.

When the denial continues it sometimes results in the loss of the home, loved ones and health. This, as well as having a dramatic impact on the life of the person in denial, can also have a knock-on effect on the lives of those around him, for many years to come.

The person in denial may make many empty promises to family and friends e.g. "We'll sort something out." He may promise to pay off some of the debts, give up his drinking and overspending. This is not to resolve his problem but to buy him time and more spending power.

What about this man's partner?

She may also be in denial. She may continue to live with him, despite the hurt and pain she is experiencing. She sees the collapse of the relationship, the devastation in the home, and the affect all of this is having on herself and the children. She believes him, because she wants to. She wants to have a functional and happy home for herself and her children. She is hoping that one day he will change. Her partner does not accept reality. He continues life as he has always done. He can be very convincing to other people. He can convince himself and others that he has adequate financial resources and has provided for everybody – (with no money to his name).

He can write numerous cheques under the pretext that he is paying his bills, but will have no money in his bank account to honour them.

As the family, financial and health pressures continue to build, his need to escape becomes greater. He can, without any conscience, move on to new surroundings. The person in denial can do this without a backward glance, leaving his past behind him. He can leave a trail of homeless, penniless people with broken hearts, broken trust and broken promises. He may be in total denial of the emotionally and mentally damaged people he has left on his path behind him. He can deny or minimise all of this, so that he does not have a sense of guilt.

This is denial at its utmost.

Persons in denial are impervious to argument, no matter what facts are placed before them. When life does not work out for them, they blame others and deny their part.

What about his friends?

They may loan him more and more money and listen to his every excuse. They continue to give him more and more chances, thinking his luck will change. People in denial may move to new relationships, new friends and new challenges without any remorse. They keep themselves busy (mental avoidance) or use substances (alcohol etc.) to deny their behaviour and the consequences of it. They may also verbally deny their part in the whole scheme of things saying, "It is no big deal, aren't you better off now?" "You are going on about nothing." It may not be until he leaves behind a number of broken homes and financial losses etc., that a person in denial seeks help or therapy.

Do you recognise yourself in any of these stories?

Are you in denial?

Have you been in denial?

Are you supporting someone in denial?

If you have been a victim or affected by a person in denial, possibly for a number of years, you may find it difficult to create closure on that time in your life. You may find it difficult at times, to move on with your life, or trust, or create new beginnings, especially if this person is still in denial as to the extent or level of hurt you have experienced as a result of their behaviour.

For the victims, closure on their hurt / abuse may be less difficult if the person in denial (the abuser) admits and acknowledges the consequences of their behaviour. The victim may need professional help to process what has happened for them, so they can begin their journey on the road to recovery.

Look at your life today and answer these questions honestly, only then can you begin the road to recovery.

If you are the person who has been living in denial, you may also need professional help to enable you to live a healthy and more functional life.

If you do not acknowledge your behaviour and the repercussions this behaviour may be having on yourself and those around you, how can you possibly change this behaviour? You must learn to take responsibility for your actions, in order for you to learn and for you to achieve your full potential on your life's journey.

(8)
The Shoes

In this story relationships are likened to a pair of shoes. Think about your current relationship and take some time to reflect upon the following questions:

Are you happy in your relationship?

Is there anything troubling you about your relationship?

Do you find your relationship comfortable or downright painful?

In this story you are being invited to consider a relationship in quite a different and novel way. The relationship is likened to a pair of shoes and you are being asked to ascertain how comfortable these shoes are to wear. In essence you are being invited to weigh up your relationship and to consider how content or otherwise you may be feeling.

Let us suppose you have a pair of shoes and you are experiencing some discomfort in them. The first option to consider is that the problem may simply be something minor and may easily be rectified. It may however be something major, which neither you nor the master shoemaker namely the Divine Power, can repair at this point in time. Since these shoes may not be suitable for you at this point in your journey, it may be time to stop wearing them.

In terms of your relationship this may mean letting go. First you must look at the reasons for the discomfort. After all would you not take a close look at your shoes if they started to hurt? These shoes might be too small or too tight and you may need to expand them a little. Wearing shoes, which inhibit your circulation, could impede and delay you on your journey. Similarly, a relationship that is restrictive and cramps your style, can cause a lot of physical, emotional and mental discomfort.

Perhaps it is just a loose heel that is causing the problem. This could represent a small issue in a relationship like one person constantly being late or not keeping promises. This behaviour can cause a lack of trust. Just like the shoes, you never know when you may be let down.

Are these particular shoes too heavy for your feet? Are they dragging you down? (Maybe there is little or no fun in your relationship?) Are you yourself a bit heavy for these shoes? (Maybe you need to "lighten up" a little in your attitudes.)

Are your shoes dull or shiny? (The question is whether your relationship is dull and dreary or light and happy. Is there any colour, variety or excitement in your relationship?)

Is there enough support in your shoes, or are they likely to let you down without warning? (Is there enough support for you in your relationship, or are you let down frequently and without warning with empty promises?)

Are you balanced in your shoes? (Is there enough give and take in your relationship?)

Would you put on a brand new pair of shoes, which were uncomfortable and then walk fifty miles in them? You could experience a lot of unnecessary pain if you did. (Would you enter into a long-term arrangement with another person in the full knowledge that you were not comfortable in their company?)

If your shoes are uncomfortable you may miss out on a lot of joy and a lot of learning opportunities, which you could otherwise avail of on your journey. You may spend most of your time buying plasters, healing cuts and bruises and getting lifts from others when you are unable to walk. This implies that you will come to depend on the support of friends, when you can no longer cope. You could also spend a lot of time sitting by the roadside (on your journey through life) in tears, as life passes you by.

Are you having any of these experiences in your life?

If so, you may need to take off your shoes for a while. You may need to stand back and take a good look at them. You may need to step out of your relationship for a while – not leave or abandon it – just step out of it. Take a good look at this relationship and ask yourself, "When and where did the shoes start to hurt first? Was it the day you fitted them on? Was it as far back as the first date you had with your partner? Was it the first day you walked a long distance in them and got blisters on your feet?" You may have felt that you had gone too far, the first time you went on holidays with this person.

Did you continue to wear these shoes regardless of the number of times they let you down, embarrassed you, left you in tears and hurt you over and over again? Is this what happened in your relationship? Were there times when you felt that you and your partner were incompatible?

As time passed did your shoes become worn out? (Did you become tired and worn out in your relationship?) You may have felt at some stage you could not change these shoes or did not know where you would find another pair. Did you really believe these shoes would adapt enough to suit your particular feet? (Did you believe that this person and this relationship would adapt enough to suit your particular needs?)

Are you going to continue wearing these shoes in the hope that you can force them to adapt to your feet?

(Are you intending to stay in this relationship and make it work for you?) It is hard struggling day and night in these shoes with so much discomfort, never knowing when they will fall apart and let you down. You may think to yourself that moving to a new house in a new neighbourhood may create a new life for you both and improve your relationship. You may be moving the shoes to a different place, but they are still the same shoes.

Do you intend to continue wearing these shoes until

they either fall off your feet or your feet are so damaged, that no other shoes will fit you? The shoes you have that may have been suitable for another pair of feet, may be so worn and battered now that they are of no use to you or anybody else. (Have you stayed in this relationship so long that both parties are worn out and battered?) There may be so much pain and anguish that neither party feels able to start another journey with a new partner.

Are you now aware that just as you could never have fundamentally changed the shape of these shoes, you could never have changed your partner or your relationship, to the extent to which you may have desired? You cannot change anyone but yourself. This may be one of the most important learnings of this lifetime for you.

Reflection:

Take a deep breath and allow yourself to relax. Consider the aspects of your current relationship, which you find uncomfortable.

- What are the communication levels like in this relationship? Can you communicate with your partner on any or all levels, or is there little or no communication between you both.
- Be really honest with yourself. Maybe you need to learn to converse more with your partner.
- Maybe you need to learn to listen more.
- Maybe neither of you feel heard, when you express to each other how you feel about different issues or problems within the relationship.
- Maybe you both need to spend more time together and see if you are truly compatible.
- Maybe you need to allow yourself to be yourself.
- Maybe your partner needs to be allowed to be himself/herself. Maybe you need help with this relationship.

Try and talk to a non-judgmental friend or relative.

Contacting a professional therapist may be of help.

Do not be afraid to ask for help.

Do not judge yourself too harshly. You worked with the knowledge you had at the time.

Prayer:

I ask my higher power to help me recognise how and when I am forcing my relationship to work (forcing my shoes to fit).

I ask my higher power to help me recognise how and when I am forcing or compromising myself to make myself fit into this relationship (this pair of shoes).

Affirmation:

Today I will spend time reflecting on my relationship.

(9)
Enabling

Are you a helper or are you an enabler?

Helpers help people to help and heal themselves.

Enablers create and allow situations where people can behave and live in an irresponsible manner.

Are you or have you been an enabler?

Are you tired and fed up?

Are you feeling that you are or have been, taken for granted by family and friends?

Do you believe you are good at helping people to sort out their problems?

Do you sometimes feel, that the more you do for people, the more they expect from you?

Do you find that family and friends regularly rely on you to sort out their domestic, emotional and financial problems?

Do you ever find when there is a crisis with family or friends; you are the first to be called upon?

Do you or have you enabled people to remain sick because it made you feel good, or because of your need to be needed?

Do you have difficulty saying "no" to others regardless of your own circumstances?

Do you know that enablers do not help others, but rather deprive them of their life's learnings and experiences?

Do you feel others are enabling or have enabled you, by continually sorting out your financial, domestic and emotional problems, and in doing so have been or are, depriving you of many of life's learnings and experiences?

You can enable someone by not allowing him or her to take responsibility for their own financial situation, or by not allowing them to realise the consequences of not creating limits on their spending, or extravagant lifestyle. You can enable them to do this, by continually paying off their debts when they overspend, or loaning them money without question, every time they request it.

You can enable partners, friends or work colleagues by continually lying about the real reason as to why they have not fulfilled their work commitments, family commitments etc.

You can enable parents by taking responsibility for the welfare of their children.

Do you enable, or have you enabled your children by constantly tidying and cleaning up after them, and not allowing them to take responsibility for the consequences of their untidiness and lack of organisation?

Do you enable or have you enabled your children or other family members, by not allowing them to pay their share towards their upkeep whilst they are living with you in your home, and are themselves earning a substantial wage?

If you are doing this, your children cannot learn how to gauge their finances, or limit their spending. How will they manage if a time comes when they have to cope and survive on their own, and you are no longer there to enable them?

Have you or do you allow your children to overspend and live beyond their means? How can they learn the repercussions of overspending, if you supply them with money every time they run short?

Do you or have you enabled your children to take regular days off work, for no specific reason other than they cannot be bothered to get out of bed? You may have allowed a belief system to develop with your children, that *you* will subsidise the shortfall in their wage packet at the end of the week. You may be out working yourself to meet your commitments and can ill afford any added expenses. By continually enabling your children, you are depriving them of some of life's most important learnings.

Story 1.

Imagine about ten years ago you decided to start a little bed and breakfast business that catered for about twelve people. You have a neighbour down the road who also has a B&B. We will call him Tom. You have been good friends with this person for years. His B&B holds approximately six people. Tom has not hesitated to borrow your car, your food, your bed linen etc., whenever he runs short. You have never refused to help this person out.

For a considerable period of time he has been overbooking his clients and availing of your space. First it was parking space, then it was a few rooms for a night or two – but now, most of your rooms are full with *his* clients. Okay, they are only sleeping and parking on your premises and he is feeding them, – but sometimes with your food.

Your business did really well until recently, when your health deteriorated and you were not able to cope as well as you would have liked. Your meal times were erratic, because of not having enough time to cook for yourself. You found yourself suffering from insomnia and getting quite depressed at times. You are now in the process of making plans to close down your B&B to give yourself some "time out," and spend more time with your family and friends.

Hearing of your intention to close down your B&B, Tom has decided to build an extension onto his B&B, to cater for the extra business, which he anticipates he will acquire when your B&B is no longer in operation.

Where did all of this begin?

It began way back the first time you enabled Tom. He never knew how much food to buy because he knew you were there to borrow from, if he ran short. He never expanded his parking area because yours was always available. He never limited himself to how many clients he booked in because he knew you would take the overflow and fit them in somewhere, even if it meant leaving your own bed and doubling up with the children.

This man has lived in denial of his own limitations for years. But it was you who enabled him to do this. For you, your feelings towards this man may now have turned from friendship, to feelings of anger and resentment. He has a big fat bank balance. You have become unwell and worn out from years of enabling someone else.

Story 2.

Imagine you have a good friend for years and neither of you ever learned to drive. You did not need to, because you both lived in town. All this was fine until both families moved to the country and lived close to each other. You eventually learned to drive because of shopping, kids to be transported to and from schools etc. You did not mind taking your friend's children to and from school, to dancing and swimming lessons and taking your friend shopping on the odd occasion.

Eventually she decides to come shopping with you every Friday. She plans her week around you. If she needs to pop out to see her parents ten miles away you take her. Since you got this car rather than being a bonus, it has now become a major hassle for you. Your time is no longer your own. You have suggested on a few occasions that it could be of benefit to your friend if she learned how to drive, but she chose to ignore your suggestion. She has told her friends that she does not need to learn how to drive, because she has *you* to drive her anywhere she needs to go. If you decide to go away for a weekend, you feel you have to take her shopping before you go.

You are beginning to resent this friend and you feel you are being taken for granted. It all comes to a head when you take her shopping one particular Friday. She does not bother to get her own trolley or bring her own shopping bags. She uses your shopping bags and piles her full load of shopping into your shopping trolley. You accidentally take one of her bags home with her Sunday roast to your house. You go away for the weekend, and come back on Monday. Your friend is furious. She had visitors for the weekend. She tells you how inconsiderate and careless you are. You are devastated and hurt by the extent of her anger, especially because of all you have done for her over the years.

Initially you were helping this person as a good friend. Eventually you were enabling her. You did not allow her to learn. Now you are not speaking to each other. She has learned to drive and she does not need you.

What do you need to learn?

The first thing you need to learn is to say "no." This can be difficult. You may have a lifetime of not being able to say "no." The next thing you can learn, is to see the difference between enabling and helping? Stop and ask yourself, "Am I helping or enabling someone?"

Enablers sometimes believe they are good, caring people, but often have a vested interest in what they are doing.

- Is there a possibility you are doing this because it can be a "make you feel good situation?"
- Is there a fear that if you allow the other person their learning, they may no longer have a need for you?

The next time you find yourself in a similar situation, take a deep breath and ask yourself, what is going on for you in this situation? Ask yourself and answer honestly, "Am I trying to help, or am I enabling this person, by not allowing them to take responsibility for their own lives?"

Affirmation:

I will learn the difference between caring and enabling.

I will learn the difference between helping and enabling.

(10)
The Thief

Is there a thief watching your house (your physical, emotional or mental body)?

The house in this story is your body. The thief is that cold, flu, virus or any other sickness or illness, that invades your body (your house) when you are busy, or when you are absent or preoccupied with other people's problems.

It may be time to check your house (your body) and see how safe and secure it is. Are you absent from your house for longer than is necessary? Check in today on how your house is. (Check in on how your body, mind and spirit are today).

How are you feeling today?

Do you feel optimistic and happy, or do you feel tired and despondent? If you feel optimistic and happy thank God, your guides, your angels and yourself for all you have.

If you are feeling tired and despondent you may need to ask yourself why? What is happening for you? Have you been busy and preoccupied with everyone and everything but yourself? Do you feel you have had little return, for all you have done for others over the years? You may have some doubts about the condition of your health. You may be feeling sad or lonely. You may be feeling dejected. You may be feeling, that nobody appears to have time for you or need you anymore.

Take a long look at your body, mind and spirit.

What do you know about your body? What age are you? How many people have you taken care of and made provisions for over the years? How many people have you provided a home for? Is your home now a bit dilapidated and run down? (Are you a bit dilapidated run down and burned out)?

Maybe it is time to return and stay a while, in the home that has provided for you over all these years. Your home (your body) is the temple for your soul. It deserves to be treated with reverence and with respect. It deserves the best you can give it. It deserves all the time and patience you can give it. It deserves to be heard when it cries out.

The longer you spend in this house (this body) the better you will know it. The better you know it, the more you will tune in to its needs. The faster you tune in to its needs, the less likely you are to have any major health problems.

Ask yourself:

- When was the last time you had a good look at your house (your body)?
- What is the longest time you have spent in your own house recently? (What is the longest time you have spent focusing on yourself recently)?
- Do you stand still, focus on yourself on a regular basis and ask yourself how you really feel?
- Do you rush out of your home most days and only return home when it is absolutely necessary i.e. when something goes wrong, burst pipes etc? (Do you leave your body most days only to return when you get a pain)?
- Are you busy minding, cleaning and repairing everybody else's house (everyone else's business)?
- Did you know you had a thief in the house, a thief who was observing all of your behaviours? How did he get in? He got in when you were out. He had been keeping your house (your body) under surveillance for some time, and entered when you left your house and forgot to come home.

Do you remember one particular day when you felt tired and unwell? You gave your neighbour a lift to town and then spent hours waiting for them. Further time was spent listening to them and trying to resolve their family problems. Time, which you badly needed to spend on yourself and your own health problems. How many similar incidences have occurred in your life? You were looking after someone else's house, (someone else's issues) but neglecting your own. This was only one of the many opportunities the thief had to get into your house.

The thief, is the cold you got last Christmas upsetting all your Christmas plans, parties and dinners. The thief, is your aches, pains and sicknesses. There may be many reasons for those aches and pains.

- Are you stressed and overworked? Are you taking other people's problems on board and carrying them around with you causing your stairs to creak? (Aches and pains in your back and neck).
- Are your shoulders aching and overburdened? Are you trying to shoulder too much responsibility for others?
- Is your kitchen in need of an overhaul? (Is your digestive system out of sync and not working properly due to poor dietary habits)?
- How are the joists, (your joints), are they creaking under the pressure?
- Is your plumbing system seizing up? (Do you have blocked arteries due to unhealthy eating habits, lack of exercise, poor maintenance)?
- How is your fireplace? What does your hearth (your heart) look like? Is it cold and empty (no love, warmth or fire in your heart) or is it full of soot and decayed embers (old hurts which have not been dealt with, cleared away or resolved)?
- Are your windows fogged up? (Are your eyes fogged up, you cannot see where you are going)?
- Are your foundations shaky? (Do you have a shaky belief system)?

- Are the doors in your house falling off their hinges? Are the locks broken? Are you unable to keep out unwanted visitors and thieves (no boundaries for yourself or others)?
- Are your walls weak and unable to support the roof? (Have you had early life traumas and a lack of support from family and friends)?
- How does the plaster look? Is it cracked and dried? (How is your skin)?
- Is your roof leaking and allowing in the harsh elements? (Are the harsh events / happenings in life seeping in and saturating your being)?

The thief came and went. You changed the locks after the break-in. (You built up your immune system and made a half-hearted attempt to change your way of being). But the next opportunity you got, you stayed out of your house for a full week, not just a few hours or days. You spent endless hours getting everyone sorted out, such as the neighbours, the kids, the football club and the parent's committee. You just did not have time to be bothered with that little pain in your chest. You thought to yourself "perhaps it is only indigestion and can be sorted out when I have time, but right now there are other much more important things to be done."

You took on all the arrangements for your daughter's wedding even down to choosing her dress. On the day of the wedding you hid your partner's money to prevent him from drinking too much and spoiling the day. You wore yourself out trying to keep everybody happy and prevent family arguments.

You have been absent from your house for some time again. The thief has been waiting for this opportunity. On the evening of the wedding, just as you thought you had everyone and everything sorted out, – he strikes again. This time the thief strikes hard. (The pain is very severe). He has broken into your house, severely damaging the plumbing system. The circulation is blocked and the pipes have clogged up. (The arteries have blocked up).

What do you do now?

Do you call the plumber (The doctor) for a quick fix, and then afterwards carry on as you always did, taking care of everything and everyone but yourself? Do you say to yourself, "Never mind I can let someone else worry about this house and let *them* give it a good overhaul." (You could go to hospital and have a good check-up, after all why should you worry, when you can always pay someone else to sort out your problems)?

The problem is that this is your house (your body) and a once off service is not going to save it. You may have to stay at home and keep vigilant day and night. (You may have to stay at home and watch your diet, take regular exercise, have regular check-ups, take care of yourself for a change, instead of involving yourself in everybody else's problems). That is if you want to save this house (this body).

This new determination may last for a month or two or until you get your strength back again. Okay you have just regained your good health, when off you go again for the next six months, to every committee meeting, club event or worthy cause, indeed anything so that you do not have to go home and take care of yourself. (Maybe you are afraid to look at your own issues; issues that you may have been trying to avoid for some time and may not feel able to deal with). You could be living in a world of denial.

This is the chance the thief has been waiting for. Now he can come and stay as long as he likes. The battle begins all over again, between you and the thief. The battle for you, is to claim back from the thief what is rightfully yours – (your good health).

By now this thief knows your every move, he has been watching you for many years. This is his time and it is do-or-die for you. He has a name and he does not mind you knowing it, because it scares even the toughest people. *You* know it too.

Where were you the first day he called? Come back before it is too late. You still have a chance, but you must act now. The longer you have been absent from your body, the longer it will take to become familiar with it and to know it again. But you *can* do it. You *can* take charge of your life and your health, – before it is too late.

What can *you* do for *you* today?

Sit down. Take a deep breath. Feel any pain or any tension in your body. Ask yourself, do you need to make that appointment with your doctor or health care professional, which you have been putting off until now? How long is it, since you really looked at and tuned in to your body?

Affirmation:

I will check every door and window in my house. I will put locks on my doors and windows where I have none. (I will create boundaries for myself and others).

I will find out what is causing the creaking in my stairs (my back).

I will check my kitchen (my digestive system, and my diet).

I will check my plaster (my skin). I will stop covering up and plastering over the issues I need to deal with.

I will check my joists for wear and tear (my joints).

I will check my plumbing (my arteries).

I will check my fireplace and my hearth (my heart). I will clear out any old soot or burned out embers (old issues) that may be preventing me from lighting a new fire (hav -ing new love and warmth in my life).

I will check my windows (my eyes) so I can see where I am going and what is happening around me.

I will check my drains. (I will check that I am not block- -ing the flow of energy through my body).

I will check my walls. (I will ask for the support I need).

I will check my foundations. I will check and see if there are any weak or damaged spots in the foundations of my life. I will heal this area of my life. I will replace these weak spots with good solid concrete. (I will make sure I have good solid concrete belief systems, that will support me in whatever I choose to do in this lifetime).

I will check my roof (my head). I will stop allowing negativity coming into my house (my life) by developing a positive outlook on life.

I will not burden myself with other people's problems or issues.

I may need help to do all of this. I will not restrict myself in availing of whatever means that are available to me, in order for me to live a long and healthy life.

I call on my God, my guides and my angels, to help me and guide me home.

(11)
Blocking The Way

Blocking the way is like the ship that is stuck in the harbour, one ship cannot move out and the other ships cannot move in.

Are you blocking somebody on his or her journey through life?

Is there someone blocking you in life?

Are you allowing yourself to go with the flow?

Are you allowing others to go with the flow?

Do you allow others to obscure your view?

Do you obscure the view of others?

Do you allow others to impede you on your journey?

Do you impede others on their journey?

How many times in life do we block the learnings of those around us, by continually providing them with answers to their problems? In doing so we are not allowing them to find answers for themselves. How many times have you said, "Hold on a minute I'll do it for you," or, "Hold on a minute I'll get it for you?" It may be more beneficial for the learning of the other person to say to them, "Wait a minute and I'll show you where it is," or, "Wait for a moment and I'll show you how to do it."

If you take a child across a dangerous road every day, without explaining how and where it is safe for them to cross the road, the child will not learn how to cross the road safely on its own. However, if you take the child to a safe place on the road and explain to them the dangers to watch out for when crossing, they will then be able to cross the road safely, on the day you are not there to help them.

If you are in a relationship where your partner has an addictive or behaviour problem, you could block the learnings for both of you:

- By covering up and lying to your partner's employers about the real reason they have not been attending work.
- By lying to the financial company as to the real reason you are both in financial difficulties.
- By lying to your family and friends as to why your partner's health is deteriorating.

You can block the learnings of family and friends by not allowing them to see, feel and experience the consequences of their behaviour: By constantly covering up and lying for them. By rectifying the mistakes they make in life. By paying bills for them as they themselves overspend on trivialities.

What you are doing in this situation is blocking the real truth of the situation.

Blocking the truth is blocking their journey, their path. If you are in a job that you feel has outlived its usefulness, fear or conditioning may be stopping you from moving on. You may not be giving this job all the energy and commitment it deserves. By staying you are blocking the way for someone else to take your position. You are also blocking someone further down the line from filling the new vacancy. You are also blocking yourself from moving on.

- Blocking the way is like keeping your ship at the entrance to the harbour in a position that does not allow others to move.
- If your ship does not move out of the way, other ships cannot get in or out.
- If you stand in a doorway, the doorway being the connection between inside and outside, you are cutting off this connection. No one can get in and no one can get out.

Example: Blocking the View.

You may believe being close to someone is always of benefit to them or to you. This is not necessarily the case. Imagine you are in a room and you are trying to explain the contents of the room to someone.

If you stand too close to this person, you obscure their view.

However, if you can take a few steps back or leave the room altogether, they can now see all they want to see. By standing too close to somebody you may not be allowing yourself a learning experience. You may also be limiting the learning experience of the other person.

You can block the way by withholding, obstructing or delaying information, which is intended for another person. You may think you are helping, but in actual fact you may be hindering.

Are you blocking the way of anyone in your life?

If you are, maybe it is time to stand back. How can someone deal with and live their lives to the fullest, if they cannot get a clear view of what is happening for them? The next time you feel inclined to block the way of others, take a deep breath and stand still for a moment.

Ask yourself, "Is this behaviour beneficial to me or the other person?"

Blocking the way is not beneficial to anyone.

How can you learn *when* you are blocking the way and how can you stop?

Do not stand in the way of someone changing, moving on, staying or leaving a job.

Do not stand in the way of someone leaving a relationship, place or situation. This may be a family member, friend or colleague. It may be their time to move on, or it may be time for you to move on and experience some new and exciting changes.

Do not cover up or try to take responsibility for the mistakes of others.

Allow others to see clearly, the consequences of their actions and behaviour.

If there are no more learnings for you where you are at, learn to step aside and allow others their learnings.

Remember the ship in the harbour; blocking the learnings of others is also blocking your own learnings.

Affirmation:

I ask my higher consciousness to bring me awareness of how, when, and why; I may be attempting to block the way of others.

I ask my higher consciousness to bring me awareness of how, when, and why; I may be blocking my own learnings.

(12)
The Cake

The story of the cake is symbolic to the story of life. The cake is life, all of life. (You are a slice of this cake, a slice of life). The ingredients in the cake are made up of all that is your life and all that has ever happened to make your life what it is today.

You may be feeling guilty about something that has happened in your life. You may be feeling responsible for that which has happened. You may feel some past action on your part, was the cause of a further chain of events.

You are responsible for everything *you* say and do, but you are *not* responsible for another person's reaction to it. You play a major part in what happens in your life, but you cannot be responsible for all that happens.

Take for example a slice of cake. There are many ingredients in this slice of cake. This slice is only part of the whole cake. The whole cake is all of life. You may not like this slice of cake, now that you have tasted it. (You may not like what life has produced, now that you have tasted it, "other people's behaviour etc"). This slice could be a friend, a partner or a family member. This slice could also be you. You are only seeing a slice of cake, (a slice of life). What you see is only part of the cake.

Do you blame yourself or others for the total product (the complete cake), rather than look at how many people may have played a part in creating the ingredients. How many more people did it take to put these ingredients together and how many more did it take to finally complete the cake? It took many lifetimes and many people to make this cake. One slice is *you.* Another slice is another person. Each of you is but a small part of the total cake.

At this point in time you may be feeling guilty and taking responsibility for all that is happening around you (the total cake). If you feel you are taking responsibility for the total happenings, it may be time to let go. Try to get in perspective the number of people, the many ingredients i.e. parents, peers, teachers, family, friends and all the scenarios it has taken, for you to reach this point where you are today.

This cake began at the beginning of time and so did you. Go back to the beginning of this cake and even further.

- Do you know what part the farmer played in harvesting the corn? Was he good or bad tempered?
- Do you know the part the person played who sold the farmer the machinery that harvested the corn? Was he honest or dishonest?
- Do you know the part the farmer's family played? Were they cruel or kind?
- Do you know the part the miller played? Was he hasty or slow?
- Do you know the part the baker played? Was he in a hurry, overworked or did he undercook or overcook the cake?
- Do you know what the shop assistant was like? Did they handle this cake with tender loving care or with aggression?
- How was your cake presented? Was it wrapped neatly or slovenly?

There are so many more people who have played a part in the making of this cake. Being the slice, is only one part of the whole (only one part of your whole life).

If you are still feeling guilty and taking responsibility for some events that have happened in your life, then it may be time to acknowledge that guilt.

Put it in perspective and say, "It is not necessarily what I would do now with the knowledge I have at this moment in time, but it was the best I could do with the knowledge I had at that time." In this way you are accepting but not denying the part you played in a particular event.

Remember guilt is a very controlling emotion but once you acknowledge it, – it loses its control over you.

Today is the day you start to move forward with responsibility for yourself, your actions and your reactions.

Affirmation:

I will acknowledge my guilt.

I will not allow guilt to control me.

I am responsible for everything I say or do.

I am not responsible for the actions or reactions of others.

I am not the total of all that is.

I am part of all that is.

I am not responsible for the total of all that is.

I am responsible for the part that is me.

(13)
Living In The moment

Do you have difficulty living in the moment?

When you find the moment, can you stay in the moment?

Do you wander back to the past and what might have been or do you wander into the future to what possibly could be?

All the time the moment is passing you by. Living in the moment is being with what is, not what was or what will be. Do you live in the present moment, or the past moment where it all went wrong, or the future moment when you are going to "get it all sorted out?"

What about starting in the present?

This is the moment you can do something about. You cannot change the past. The breakfast you ate this morning is just as past as the one you ate twenty years ago. You can never eat that breakfast again, and like all happy or painful memories, you can never experience that exact experience ever again. You can learn from your experiences and move on from them, but you will never actually experience them again.

- You were not living in the moment when you went to the clothes line and left the back door open, only to find when you returned the cat had helped himself to the roast you left de-frosting on the worktop.
- You were not living in the moment when you put on an egg to boil and then spent an hour on the telephone – now you have no egg and a burned saucepan.
- You were not living in the moment when you sat down at the table to have some breakfast and cut your finger as you were slicing bread. You drifted into the future

thinking about tomorrow's shopping, but the pain in your finger very quickly brought you back to this moment in time. However for you this may be only a temporary return to the present moment.

The future moment is how you are planning to go to the bank, as you are reminiscing over your lost egg, and the repercussions regarding your roast. You are also thinking about taking an extra half hour lunch break to go and do some shopping. You are planning to come home a little earlier and clear out your room, which reminds you, what about the burned saucepan etc?

Your head is in the future but you have not even left the table yet. You are here in body only. You have already "lived" the rest of today, tonight and part of tomorrow, without even moving from the table today.

Now the next step is to get yourself to work. You walk out to your car turn on the ignition and nothing happens. This is a moment you had not allowed for. Your car will not start, and what happens next is that your mind takes off again on yet another tangent. You start to think, "What will happen if I am late for work?" "My boss has already warned me that if I am late for work one more time, he will dismiss me." Now you start to think, "If I lose my job and I am out of work, I will have no money to pay for my car. The finance company will repossess it. I will never be able to travel anywhere or get another job again."

It has not even occurred to you to find out what is wrong with the car. Your mind goes on, and on, and on.

COME BACK!!

You were so busy planning today's busy schedule, that you passed by the petrol station last night, not noticing the red "empty" warning light flashing on your petrol gauge.

All this worrying and living in a different moment can be called "awfulizing."

Take a deep breath, and ask yourself, what can you do about the situation you are now in?

"Awfulizing" did not get you very far, so why not try some real action. You could phone the garage or a friend, and ask them to bring you some petrol. You could then phone your workplace and explain that you will be late. Now you are back in control of your life again.

Now you are living in the moment.

You get to work and back home again. You decide to go for a nice stress-free leisurely walk. After a short while it begins to rain. Now the mind starts to work overtime again – "The clothes are on the line and are going to get wet, but then maybe I can put them in the clothes dryer, oh no, that would be using up more electricity – more rows." "Peter's football boots were left out to dry. I just remembered the dog is out as well – he will tear the boots to pieces – another €150 down the drain."

So much for your nice stress-free walk! You run all the way back home, only to find the dog is still in his shed, and what is more – it never actually rained at your house at all.

It did feel that you were out of control when you were doing today's work yesterday and tomorrow's work today.

You have no control over the future.

You cannot change the past.

There is only the moment you are in right now.

Take a deep breath and repeat:

Slow me down God. Help me to live in the moment.

Affirmation:

I will live in the present moment, not in the past and not in the future.

If I wander God, help me to come back to the present.

I will take time out for myself and learn to relax.

I will enrol in some meditation, relaxation or yoga classes.

You cannot ride a horse that has not arrived.

You cannot stop a horse that has not started.

You can only do something with the horse, you have now in this moment.

... Solomon.

(14)
The Butterfly

Some say our children are on loan to us.

Some say we as parents are chosen by our children in order that they can learn from us.

When a butterfly flies into your garden (when a child comes into your life) is it your butterfly? (Does this child belong to you?)

If the butterfly decides to stay in your garden and feed in your garden – do you have a claim on this butterfly? (When a child decides to stay with you into adulthood, do you have a claim on this child?) If the butterfly decides to stay and lay eggs in your garden, are these eggs your eggs?) (If your children remain with you and produce grandchildren, are the grandchildren also yours?)

When the young butterfly has learned all he wants to learn in your garden, do you stop him from moving on to newer pastures, new learnings? (When your children have learned all you can teach them, do you stop them from moving to new pastures, new learnings?)

Once this butterfly learned to fly, he had the choice whether he stayed in your garden or moved to another one. (Once your children learn to spread their wings and fly they are no longer your responsibility. They also have the choice, whether to stay with you, or move on.)

Do you clip the butterfly's wings so that he is limited in how far he flies? (Do you do this with your child? Do you limit his freedom, limit his growth and limit his knowledge?) Do you fear that if you give him unlimited freedom, he may not return? (Do you have this fear around your child/children? Do you clip your children's wings because you have a fear of losing them?)

Are you allowing your children to learn and grow with life's experiences and learnings?

- Do you give them unconditional love, help and support to assist them on their journey?
- Do you limit the resources and information that you give to your children, thereby restricting their learnings and freedom?
- Do you have a fear they will survive without you?
- When the butterfly leaves your garden, do you lock the gate so he cannot return?
- When he returns, do you lock the gate so he cannot escape or do you leave the gate unlocked, so he can come home to rest whenever he needs to? (Do you do the same with your children? When you see a child whether it is your own or someone else's, know they are learning how to fly. No one but the child knows when he or she will be ready.)
- Can you allow the space in your garden for the butterfly to learn, without conditions or limitations? (Can you allow the space in your life for a child to learn, whether it is your own or someone else's? Most of all can you give them the freedom to fly when they are ready?)

Your children are on loan to you, and have decided to visit your garden for a time and share your learnings and life's experiences. When these learnings are complete, your children need to be allowed to spread their wings and move to different pastures, learnings and experiences and to enjoy all that life has to offer.

Remember you too are also like the butterfly. Like the butterfly, at all times you have free will and freedom of choice as to which garden you choose to live in and how long you decide to live there. This is always how it was whether you were aware of it or not.

There was a time when you flew into someone's garden and you stayed there for whatever length of time they allowed you to stay there, or for whatever length of time you found it was necessary for you to experience your learnings.

Did your parents have difficulty in giving you your freedom?

Do you have difficulty letting go and giving freedom?

Affirmation:

I am free

I give freedom.

(15) Panic Attacks

Do you feel there are times when you are unable to cope with what is happening in your life, not even for one more minute?

Are there times when you also feel even the good things that are happening for you are too much for you to cope with?

Do you feel your pulse is constantly racing, your heart is pounding and you have difficulty breathing properly? Your life, which appeared to be going at a nice steady pace, may now appear to have speeded up considerably. You may feel you are out of control of your life. Do you sometimes feel a sense of panic without any known cause, at least not any cause you can identify with? If you can relate to any of these feelings, it is time to stop. Stop and find out what is causing these feelings. Find out what you can do for you.

What are panic attacks?

Those feelings of anxiety or panic can be suppressed in the area of the solar plexus. The solar plexus is the energy centre or "chakra" between the sternum and the naval. The feelings or emotions in this centre are anxiety, anger and fear. Your "gut feeling" is felt in the solar plexus.

Imagine a wardrobe jammed packed full of clothes. One day you decide to squeeze in one more T-shirt. The wardrobe falls apart and the entire contents of the wardrobe comes tumbling out.

Some of these clothes are your own. (Your own belief systems).

Some do not fit you anymore. (You have changed some of your belief systems).

Some you have had for so long they are out of fashion, outdated. (Outdated belief systems).

There are other clothes in this wardrobe that do not even belong to you. (Other people's belief systems and conditioning).

Some you borrowed and forgot to return. (You took other people's opinions and beliefs on board and kept them).

Others belong to people who did not have any more use for them so you allowed them to dump them on you. (You allowed others to dump their rubbish on you).

What do you do?

Do you blame the T-shirt or yourself or someone else or the wardrobe? Was the wardrobe too small or the T-shirt too bulky? Could it be that there was simply too much rubbish building up in your wardrobe for many years?

See your body like the wardrobe:

- When it is overloaded and collapses, do you call someone in to fix it?
- Do you pick up all the clothes and other bits of rubbish off the floor and squeeze them all back in again?
- Do you blame someone else for packing your wardrobe too tightly?
- Do you take the last item you tried to force in there, and blame it for breaking the wardrobe?
- Or, do you sort it all out and only place back in the wardrobe what you really need?

You may have tolerated insults, hurts and rejections most of your life, until one day someone says the wrong thing at the wrong time and you finally "blow your top." You explode with anger and frustration. Your body just cannot take any more. The reaction is panic and alarm. The slightest feeling of pressure can send you over the top. You cannot take any more.

This is what could be referred to as a panic attack, (or an overflow of feelings).

Take a deep breath and as you exhale, allow your body to relax. (Repeat this exercise three times).

Read the poem "Slow Me Down God" at the end of this story. Read the poem on a regular basis until you know it off by heart.

When you feel a sense of panic, take a deep breath and say "Slow me down, God." Continue until your body and mind has relaxed.

When the feeling of panic has passed, ask yourself what is happening in your overall life.

What is going on for you at the time you feel a sense of panic?

- Have you taken on too much responsibility for too many people and too many tasks?
- Have you made too many commitments to too many people?
- Have you allowed other people's belief systems to control you?

For long term benefits:

Try and recognise when enough is really enough for you.

Try and find time to unwind and relax on a regular basis.

Purchase a relaxation tape so that you can relax in the comfort of your own home.

Think about joining a relaxation, meditation or yoga class.

Read the story on "Overwhelm."

Slow me down God:

Slow me down God. Ease the pounding of my heart by the quieting of my mind. Steady my hurried pace with the vision of the eternal reach of time.

Give me, amidst the confusion of my day, the calmness of the everlasting hills. Break the tensions of my nerves and muscles with the soothing music of the singing streams that live in my memory.

Help me to know the magical, restoring power of sleep. Teach me the art of taking one-minute vacations – of slowing down to look at a flower, to chat with a friend, to pat a dog, to read a few lines from a good book, to go for a nice leisurely walk, to dream.

Remind me each day of the fable of the hare and the tortoise that I may know that the race is not always to the swift – that there is more in life than increasing speed.

Let me look upward into the branches of the towering oak and know that it grew great and strong because it grew slowly and well.

Slow me down God, and inspire me to send my roots deep into the soil of life's enduring values that I may grow upward toward the stars of my greater destiny.

*Author unknown.

(16)
Control

Are you a controller?

Are you allowing yourself to be controlled?

Control is a word used regularly in today's society e.g. "She / He is a control freak."

What exactly does this mean? It means that anyone who tries to control another person for their own gain is a controller. Controllers are not always consciously aware of their need to control or how, or why, their controlling tactics work. When a controller feels he/she is controlling a situation they may feel that they are safe and more secure. Controllers are constantly trying to maintain control over one situation or another, or one person or another.

Are you a controller, or do you know someone who is a controller, or who tries to be a controller?

*("He" and "him" will be used instead of he / her / they to simplify this explanation).

A controller can only control when someone allows themselves to be controlled. As long as a controller finds their controlling behaviour works for them, they will continue to behave in this way.

- If you are using controlling behaviours, you need to be aware of the affects this may be having on yourself and on others.
- If you are the victim of somebody else's controlling behaviours and you become aware of this, you may need to make a decision whether you wish to remain in this situation or not.

There are many different types of controllers. There are many different tactics, which may be used as a means to control others.

- Controlling through guilt.
- Controlling through fear.
- Controlling through silence.
- Controlling by being nice.
- Controlling by aggression.
- Controlling by lying.
- Controlling through arrogance.
- Controlling by manipulation.

We may sometimes have learned to control or we may have been controlled from an early age.

As tiny babies we may learn that if we cry for long enough, we will be picked up out of our cots. As young children we learn one of the best times to get attention or get something, which we would not normally be allowed, would be at the checkout in the local supermarket. By crying or throwing tantrums, our parents could become embarrassed and are more likely to give in to our demands. Another time we can learn how to get what we want is when relatives or friends come visiting. Our parents may not wish to appear mean or unkind, again they may "give in" to our demands to stop us from throwing tantrums in front of the guests.

As we grew older and attended college, we may have applied controlling tactics, like making our parents feel guilty when we were asked to do our share of household duties by exclaiming, "How can I pass my exams if I do not have enough time to study?" But we will find all the time necessary for socialising, having fun and spending hours on the phone. When we wish to avoid doing something we dislike, we may again resort to our controlling tactics. When using controlling tactics to get the desired results, we need to be aware of how these behaviours may be affecting others. Controlling behaviour is dysfunctional behaviour.

Controlling through guilt.

Do you control through guilt? Do you try to make someone feel guilty, if they do not meet your demands? Do you try to make someone feel guilty, by demanding more time, or more money than they can afford to give you? Do you remind someone of all you have done for them in the past, when they do not succumb to your wishes? The person being controlled may try to fulfil your wishes from a sense of guilt, not because they love or care about you.

Is there someone in your life who controls you through guilt? Are you staying in a job, a relationship or remaining in a family situation, because of a sense of guilt? Are you staying, not because you care about someone or love them, but because you feel beholden to them, because of all they have done for you?

Do you have memories from the past where you were given "the guilty treatment" when you did not satisfy someone else's needs or requirements, e.g. in school – not getting better exam results, in sports – not achieving enough by other people's standards, in work – not achieving higher results by other people's standards?

Do you control through fear?

Do you live in or create situations where someone will be fearful of what you may say, or what you may or may not do, if they do not behave in a certain way? Have you ever threatened to harm yourself or others if you did not have your demands met? Have you ever threatened to leave a job or relationship if the other person did not succumb to your wishes or requests? This other person, friend, partner or relative may give in to your wishes, only because you are triggering in them, a memory of fear and guilt where in the past you or someone else carried out their threats with devastating consequences?

The threatened person is not complying with your wishes because they love or care about you, but because of the fear of what you might do. They may feel they will not be able to live with the guilt, should you go through with your threats. You are now attempting to control this person through fear.

Are you yourself being controlled through fear?

Are you being controlled by the fear or the threat of what will happen if you leave a job, a relationship or a family situation? Are you fearful of the consequences and the affect it will have on you and those around you, if you leave? Are you staying in a job or relationship because someone says, "Think what it could do to your family or friends if you leave this job, home or relationship – it could have a devastating affect on them?"

It can also be fear of the criticism, rejection or disappointment from family or friends that can control you and stop you moving on with your life. Allowing yourself to be controlled in this way can be detrimental to your emotional and mental well-being.

Do you control by silence?

The subtlest type of control of all is silence. Nobody knows what the problem is, if you stay silent. One person is blaming the other for upsetting you, while still wondering if they were the ones who did or said something to upset you. In a job situation you may feel annoyed with someone, or about some issue relating to your work, but rather than talk about it, – you go silent. Now nobody knows who has upset you this time, so everybody is humouring you, placating and walking on eggshells, in case it was them who offended you. This behaviour can be a learned behaviour tactic to get attention and to try and control those around you. There can be many reasons for silence. Silence in a person is not always about control, but sometimes it can be a controlling technique.

As an adult you may have a childhood memory of a controlling tactic that worked in a family situation. The child may have discovered that being silent for a certain length of time, brought the parent's focus of attention on them. The child may have also discovered, that this could be a way of getting undivided attention from his parents, teachers or friends. Getting attention is not always the reason for silence, but it can be a learned behaviour tactic to get attention.

A child, who has written on the blackboard without the consent of his teacher, can by his silence, control his fellow pupils and his teacher. The teacher detains the entire class until someone admits to the offence. The fear of the consequence may deter the pupil from admitting his offence, but his silence is nonetheless controlling the entire class.

Are you yourself being controlled by silence?

When someone is silent and non communicative in your presence, do you sometimes feel you must have done or said something to upset them? Does silence trigger childhood memories for you of your parents or other family members or friends arguing and fighting, and then the endless silence following the argument, and you the child feeling fearful and apprehensive, not knowing when the rows and arguments might begin again?

The silence for a child in a situation like this can be quite terrifying, because in the silence, they never know when things are finally going to go wrong again. The child may try to fill the void in the silence by continually asking questions, by incessant chattering, by crying without having any obvious reason for doing so, by argumentative or irritating behaviour towards fellow siblings, by constantly endeavouring to please, or by doing chores they would not normally do.

Memories may now be triggered for you as adult, memories where silence meant uncertainty and unsafety for you as a child. The belief system may now be, "You must break the silence or fix the cause." Your behaviour as an adult may now be controlled by the silence of those around you. You may need to learn where and when silence is appropriate and acceptable. It does not always mean you have done something wrong or something is about to go wrong.

Do you control by being nice?

You have heard the expression "He/She is so nice today,

they must be looking for something." The nice controllers are difficult to detect. They can lull you into a false sense of security and most times you may fall for it. You may do this, or someone you know may be a nice controller. This person calls on you out of the blue, bearing useless or outdated gifts, for which you have little or no use. They may seem genuine at the time, but as they are about to depart, they ask you if you would take care of their dog for two weeks while they go away on holidays, or they could ask you, if you would mind if they borrowed your new mobile home by the sea for the weekend.

At other times they may call and want to borrow money or other items, such as your lawnmower, your trailer, your car etc. You may find it difficult to refuse, because they have given you a gift or present. These efforts at being nice could be questionable, especially if these people only call bearing gifts on very rare occasions and then look for something from you in return.

What about the person who doesn't call you for months at a time and then, "out of the blue," they are passing through your local town, and invite you out to dinner? This is not necessarily because they care about you, but more often because they have no one else to join them for dinner at the time. (You are just filling a gap as they are passing through).

What about the person who offers to bring your child home from school and mind him for the evening? They did not do this because they were being nice or caring, but rather, that they are in need of a child minder for *their* three children, the following week. Because of this person caring for your child one evening, you now feel obliged to pay this person back for something you did not ask for in the first place. Do you yourself use ulterior (or nice) behaviour patterns in order to get something in return? If you do, you are not being nice, – you are being manipulative and controlling.

Controlling through aggression.

A child sometimes learns that if he kicks and screams he will have his demands met. Are you controlling others through verbal, physical or emotional aggression? Many people have a fear of aggressive behaviour. The aggressor may believe that aggressive behaviour achieves the desired results. The aggressor sometimes will go to whatever lengths he feels will have his needs met, regardless of the consequences.

A boss or workmate who is verbally aggressive towards his fellow workers, may feel he is in control of all those around him and what they are doing. What he does not realise, is that he cannot control anyone but himself. His fellow workers or employees may remain working with this controller for only as long as they need to, or, until they can obtain other means of employment elsewhere. They will move away from this controller at the first available opportunity.

Physical or emotional aggression and attempts at controlling others through aggression can be seen regularly in the home, in public places, in work places, sports venues etc. In a relationship, after a number of outbursts of aggression, one partner (the controller) can keep the other partner submissive and under their control, because of the submissive person's fear of upsetting them and causing another outburst of aggressive behaviour. The possibility for the submissive partner, of an outburst of aggressive behaviour in the home, especially where children are involved, or in a public place where it can cause shame and embarrassment, can be very controlling, because of the possible long-term consequences this person's behaviour could have on the children or others.

Some people will have the courage to confront the aggressor, who may have been a bully for years. If you are being controlled by aggressive behaviour, you must remember that as long as the controller continues to behave in this way, and you and others allow themselves to be controlled by them, there is no reason for the controller to change their behaviour. This may be a lifetime pattern of survival for the controller, who also may have been bullied or controlled in the past. The question you must ask yourself is, "Do I wish to continue allowing myself and my life to be controlled in this manner?"

Controlling by manipulation:

As in all cases of control both male and female are equally capable of manipulation. Manipulators have only one purpose in mind, and that is to have and get what they want regardless of the damage it is doing to others.

This person can lead a double standard of life. We will speak of the male manipulator in this example. He may continue to live a relatively normal family life, with his partner/wife and children, but he may also have made a commitment to another woman. He can engage in a normal physical relationship with his wife, without her having any suspicions about this other woman. He has more difficulty engaging at an emotional or mental level, because if things are harmonious in the home, he has no excuse for storming out after an argument. He will instigate an argument, so that he will feel justified in leaving, sometimes not returning home again for days or even weeks at a time.

This person can manipulate many people at the same time, business colleagues, family, friends, etc., in order to support his lifestyle, and to cover up for his behaviour. Initially the other woman may be blamed for this man's behaviour.

When he goes missing, he may have many excuses, including telling his wife he is job searching. He may even say that he is attending for counselling to help him deal with problems in his home and place of work. He tells the other woman that his wife is a raging alcoholic and a madwoman, but that he can't leave her just yet, because of the children.

Eventually his wife finds out about the other woman. The first thing he does, is deny all knowledge, but later after many rows and arguments, he admits to the truth of his behaviour and to the fact that he had been lying all along. He once again convinces his wife that he loves her and the children. It is not long before he reverts back to the old behaviour patterns. He instigates a row, storms out, and goes back to the other woman.

He is possibly operating the same scenario with the

other woman, which gives him an opportunity to return to his wife and children. He will return to the family home on numerous occasions, full of guilt and remorse, saying the relationship with this other person is finished. His wife continues to allow herself to be manipulated physically and mentally, despite the affects his coming and going is having on herself and the children.

His wife eventually gives him an ultimatum. She tells him she wants a separation if he doesn't change his behaviour. – This works for a short while. To try and avoid this happening, the manipulator tells his wife, "She is the only person he ever really loved, or will ever love." She believes him once again, so they go for counselling separately and together. His wife later discovers that he is expressing the same sentiments to this other woman.

Whatever love, care and trust existed between this couple, may now be destroyed beyond repair. His wife and children are hurt, angry and devastated. Their physical, emotional and mental health may now be severely affected. This man has also caused financial chaos and ruin. His family may be penniless and homeless. Because of all of this, his wife now seeks a separation.

The manipulative controller can be ruthless. He can engage in many extreme behaviour patterns, from being aggressive, nasty and abusive to being nice, considerate, caring, loving, humouring, telling each person what he believes they need to hear i.e. "You are beautiful." "You are the most important person in the world to me." "You are the only person I have ever loved." "Nobody understands me like you do." "I had to work so hard." "She spent all my money."

The manipulator can also play the victim role very effectively until he has the other woman convinced of how life dealt him such a raw deal. "I got married too young." "I stayed because of the children." "We were never compatible."

What about the other woman?

The other woman may be working from a sense of low self-esteem, and have a deep need to be loved and appreciated. This person can hand over large amounts of money or goods, in order to facilitate this manipulator, (not knowing the true story).

When this person refuses to continue financing this manipulator, or the finance runs out, this manipulator can turn to physical, verbal, or abusive behaviour, sometimes seriously physically, emotionally, and mentally damaging the other person. This manipulator can switch moods so fast the other person can never relax.

This manipulator takes all he needs from this other woman, – his morale is boosted, his pockets are full, he has had a marvellous social time, wining and dining, he has enjoyed his holidays abroad, all paid for by this other woman. At this stage she may become needy and demanding, and look for something in return for all she has given him. She may demand more of his time and attention, also maybe a long-term commitment from him. The problem is that the seemingly endless supply of money from this woman may be running out. When she explains this to him this manipulator can say, "If you really cared about me you would find more money somewhere. You could get yourself another part-time job, or sell that site your parents gave you. We will buy another site together, when I am free of my marriage." (This manipulator could have been out of work for several years and has no intention of working or sharing an honest healthy relationship with anybody).

When this woman does not comply with his wishes he becomes disinterested and bored with her. Now that the victim of this manipulator has eventually outlived her usefulness, this manipulator can feel justified in ending this relationship, moving on, and creating a similar scenario somewhere else, with somebody else.

This manipulator can engage in a number of relationships at the same time. He tells each person a different story. He tells his wife that this woman has him persecuted, phoning and texting him day and night. He tells the other woman that his wife won't give him a divorce, or that she (the other woman) will have to wait until his children are older, or that he will have his divorce settled very soon so they can then spend their lives together.

It is sometimes only after irreparable loss of health and irretrievable financial losses, that the victims of this manipulator seek help and guidance. The victims may need to look at the reason behind why they allowed themselves to be manipulated. When they realised that they were being manipulated for another person's gains, they may need to ask themselves, what stopped them from discontinuing this relationship? Was it fear of more abuse? Was it fear of not being needed? Was it shame that family and friends would discover the truth about the relationship? Was it low self-esteem, or low self-worth? Was their self-worth based on what they could give this person or on how the manipulator valued them?

These persons may need help and support from family and friends. They may also need professional help to heal from the hurtful behaviour of the manipulator.

When you manipulate you hurt. When you allow yourself to be manipulated, you allow yourself to be hurt.

Controlling through lying.

The person who controls through lying can control many people at the same time. A boss in a job can promise his workers an increase in their wages if they remain working for him, knowing full well that the finance is not available for him to do this. The workers may continue to work for him, and believe this person for months and sometimes years until they eventually find out the truth. A boss can control a number of people, by promising the same job to each one of them. Each one believes the job is theirs and so live their lives accordingly, borrowing money in anticipation of the extra finances that have been promised and living a standard of life they cannot afford.

The controller through lying, deceit and making false promises, can control the lives of many people. This type of controlling is cruel; because the controller may be fully aware of the devastating affect this behaviour is having on all those concerned. It is sometimes only after many years of trauma that the controlling liar is detected. By this time many people will have been affected and scarred for the rest of their lives.

Control through arrogance.

The belief system with this type of controller can be that his time is more important than anyone else's. He can control family, friends, workmates or sport colleagues, by promising that he will do something, or that he will be at a certain place and time, knowing full well that he has made a prior arrangement with someone else.

This person can promise to be at a certain place at a prearranged time, but because of his total disregard and lack of respect for other people and their time, he will either arrive late or not at all. This person can delay a full busload of people, a major function, an important meeting or just one individual.

This type of controller rarely informs anybody that he is going to be late, or that he does not intend to turn up at all. The reason why it is important to inform someone that there is a change in the prior arrangement, is that it will free up the other person / persons and allow *them* to decide whether to wait for him or continue without him. The controller will not give the information, which will free up those who are waiting because in doing so he will no longer feel he is in control of the situation.

The arrogant controller may know someone is standing at a door waiting to be let in, and say to himself or others, "Let him wait, he can wait until I am ready." This controller can leave his workmates waiting for him on a building site. He knows unless he completes a particular job, the next stage of the job cannot commence.

Knowing his family are sitting in the car and ready to start on a journey, this controller can return back to the house for something minor and decide to make numerous phone calls. Because of this behaviour pattern, his family now refuse to get into the car unless he gets in first. What this controller fails to understand, is that over a period of time when family and friends have been on the receiving end of his poor time keeping, and lack of respect for them or their time – they in turn because of his inevitable late arrival may now turn up late for any meetings with him.

This controller does not really see the knock-on effect of his behaviour, until one day a friend promises to meet him and take him to a very important job interview. The friend already aware of the controller's poor time keeping arrives late. The controller, failing to arrive for the interview at the prearranged time, loses the job.

There can be many similar experiences for this controller. Nobody believes him anymore. They see little point in telling him the starting times of parties, meetings or social events and see little or no point in agreeing to meet him at a prearranged time.

When confronted the controller rather than apologise for arriving late or for not turning up at all, can sometimes attempt to minimise his behaviour, to the annoyance of the other person / persons delayed by his behaviour. He may exclaim, "The man who made time made plenty of it." How often have you yourself said, or heard someone else say, "I got delayed?" When the truth of the matter was, that you, or they, did not leave a particular place on time in order to get to the destination at the prearranged time.

Like any other type of control, the arrogant controller may not be doing this at a conscious level. When we become aware that we are allowing ourselves to be controlled or that we are attempting to control others, we have choices and can decide whether we continue to do so or whether we allow this controlling of ourselves to continue or not.

Because of his behaviour this controller can miss out on many joyful and happy moments in life. They can also lose out on the many learnings life has to offer.

A person with addictive behaviour patterns can use many different methods of controlling.

Family or friends may allow or enable this behaviour to continue because of the fear of what the addict may or may not do. A family may allow this controlling behaviour to continue for years. Sometimes they may do this, because of a memory of how a relative or friend behaved in similar circumstances e.g. got angry, stormed out, crashed the car, injuring themselves and someone else.

The person with the drink or drug related problem might try to manipulate and control social occasions, parties or family gatherings. The family, partner or friends of this person because of past experience, possibly also memories in early childhood of drink or drug related problems in the home, can very easily allow themselves to be controlled. This is because of the fear of aggressive or destructive behaviour by the controller. The memory of the hurt, pain and shame may be triggered, so they will do almost anything to keep those memories suppressed. This allows the controller to continue with his behaviour.

Some people use a number or combination of controlling tactics at the same time depending on how they achieved the desired results in the past.

If you are a controller, you are a jailer,

but you are also a prisoner.

Affirmation:

I will not allow myself to be controlled.

I will not attempt to control others.

I realise that I cannot control anyone but myself.

(17)
The Bicycle

It could be a time for your physical, emotional, mental and spiritual check-up.

Have you checked your life's pattern recently?

In this story the bicycle is likened to your body.

How are you peddling through life? Are you going fast or slow? Are you able to stop or slow down when and if you need to?

Can you remember when you last carried out a complete overhaul on your bicycle? (When did you last have a complete check-up on your body, mind and spirit)?

Have you checked to see if your wheels are balanced, or are they buckled and warped? How balanced are you on your bicycle? Are you wobbling all over the place? (How balanced is your life? Do you get sufficient rest, good food, exercise, fresh air, sunshine etc? Do you have emotional and mental stability in your life? Do you have enough love and joy in your life)?

Have you checked your wheels for flat or worn tyres? Are your tyres flat and worn out due to too much weight on them or too much wear and tear? (Too many late nights, poor diet, not enough rest and not enough "time out").

Did you pump up your tyres when they went flat or did you carry on peddling away regardless? Did you try and find out what might have caused them to go flat in the first place? (When you first became ill did you pump yourself up with pills etc., or did you try and find the cause of your illness)?

Were there times when your tyres went flat and you did not even bother to get off your bicycle to find out what was causing the problem? Did you rim the wheel and destroy the tyres beyond repair? (When you felt unwell did you just carry on regardless of the damage it was doing to your health)?

Did you continue to carry other heavy passengers and push yourself beyond your limit? (Did you continue to work, play sport and take on board other people's problems and issues, even though you knew you were damaging your health)?

What are the brakes like on your bicycle? (Do they allow you to slow down or stop, if and when you need to i.e. when you become unwell and your body is telling you to slow down, or, are they loose and not working properly)?

In an emergency will your brakes work efficiently enough to prevent you from running into a wall and seriously injuring yourself? Is it possible you have no brakes at all on your bicycle? Are there times when you feel you are going downhill and unable to stop yourself? (Do you feel your health is going downhill and there is little you can do to help yourself? Do you stop and find the cause and then take responsibility for your ill-health?)

Is there any light on your bicycle? (Can you see where you are at in life or where you are going? Is there any light in your life? Can you see fun, joy, good food and happiness in your life?)

What are the handlebars like on your bicycle? Are they crooked? Can you get a proper grip on them? (Do you have a problem coming to grips with your life or getting a handle on life? Are you in a job, relationship or home that you can enjoy and where you can live life to the full?)

Are you too heavy for your bicycle? (Are you overweight? Do you overburden yourself physically, emotionally or mentally?)

Will this bicycle support you for the rest for your life? (Do you have a reliable support system to last you for the rest of your life i.e. health, family, friends, finance etc?)

When your bicycle started to creak did you have it overhauled or did you push it at the same pace as you had done for many years previously? (When your body started to show symptoms of tiredness and ill health, did you continue to push it at the same rate as you did when you were many years younger?)

Have you been loaning your bicycle to others who have little or no value on it? (Have you been handing over your power, your time and your money to people who have no value on them, or respect for you?)

What does this bicycle look like now? (How do you look now? How do you feel? How is your physical, emotional and mental health?)

What can you do about this bicycle? (What can you do about you?)

You can get it completely overhauled and repaired where necessary. (You can have a complete check-up and find out what can be done about your health and how and when you can have these repairs carried out if necessary).

When your bicycle has been repaired (when your health is back in order) how do you keep it that way?

- Do not allow any more pressure on this bicycle than is absolutely necessary. (Do not allow any more pressure on yourself than is absolutely necessary).
- Do not allow anyone else to put pressure on your bicycle. (Do not allow others to put pressure on you).
- Take any extra weight off your bicycle. (Deal with your baggage i.e. problems, issues, any dysfunctional behaviour, unhealthy habits or possible diet and weight related problems). Get help to do this if necessary.
- Do not loan your bicycle to anyone unless you know they will take good care of it. (Do not give away your time, your finance etc., indiscriminately. Check first and make sure it will be valued, taken care of, and appreciated).

- If you feel you do not have a sense of where you are at or where you are going, do not be afraid to seek help and direction.
- Learn to use your brakes whenever you need to slow down, or when you feel you are going too fast. (Learn to know your limits when it comes to yourself and those around you.)
- Learn that you can give yourself permission to slow down, relax and stop if necessary.
- Learn to put the brakes on whatever is damaging your health.
- Learn how to repair and take care of your bicycle. (Learn how to repair and take care of your own body, mind and spirit. Learn how to take care of yourself. Learn self-help techniques. Learn to value your health, your time and your money).
- When your bicycle is creaking, tired, slowing down, and finding it difficult to keep on going, you must learn when and how to stop peddling. (Take time out to rest and find the cause. If you stop in time the problem may not be serious. If you continue peddling and keep on going when there is a problem with your health, you may cause more serious problems).

When your body is aching, tired and feels like it can't keep going any longer, take the time to find the cause. When you find the cause of the problem, you are halfway to the cure. If this bicycle is in a poor state of repair, you may need professional help. (If your body is in poor health you may need professional help i.e. your medical practitioner, therapist etc).

Affirmation:

Today I will give myself permission to take time out to rest.

I will make the necessary arrangements to get a complete check-up on my body, mind and spirit.

(18)
A Spiritual Journey

How do you look?

How do you feel?

Are you on your Spiritual Journey?

Do you think or maybe believe, you are or have been working hard on your spiritual journey?

Are you battering away, criticising, condemning, rejecting, analysing, blaming and pushing yourself?

Are you searching, reading and planning on what you will do when your journey does begin?

Do you believe that somewhere down the road, life really will begin for you?

Are you impatient with yourself because you are not getting there fast enough? Not learning fast enough? Not healing fast enough? Not discovering your inner-self fast enough?

Do you believe you are already on your spiritual journey or maybe have it almost completed?

If you believe that the above is your spiritual journey you may need to read on.

Imagine a very large timber box made of beautiful oak.

This box is you. This is the great being that you are. This is all of you inside and outside. You may be able to see the outside of this box, but you may also have an awareness of what is inside the box.

- How was this box made? Was it made with love or with anger?

- How does it look? (How do you look, how do you feel)?
- Is it painted all over, covering the cracks? (Have you been covering up and painting over issues and problems in your life)?
- Is it all out of proportion? (Is your life in proportion, your physical, emotional and mental health or are you all out of proportion)?
- Is this box solid? (Are you solid in your belief systems or are you easily moved, even though it is not for your greater good or the greater good of others)?
- Is this box empty? (Do you feel empty? Do you make empty promises to yourself and others or do you treat yourself well with the good things in life)?
- Is this box stuffed to capacity to the point of overflow (where you cannot take anymore)?
- Is this box at breaking point? (Are you at breaking point)?

Nobody but you knows what really is in this box. Some or all of what is in this box may have been stuffed in there many years ago or over many years. You may have stuffed it to capacity or you may have allowed or helped others to pack it to capacity or to breaking point. You may have forgotten what you have put in this box or why.

- Do you know what is holding this box together (holding you together?)
- Is it held together with old rusty screws, nails, and hinges etc., that someone else dumped, someone who had no further use for them? Is it *their* rubbish that is filling your box and holding it together (other people's belief systems and conditioning?)
- Is this box well held together? (Are you well held together? Do you have a strong belief system?)

- Is this box barely held together, frayed at the edges? (Are you frayed at the edges, frayed nerves?)
- Is the lid tightly screwed down so that no one can get in, and worse still, you cannot get out? (Do you keep a tight lid on life at all costs, never really sharing or allowing others to share your life with you?)
- Are the hinges on the lid rusty and difficult to move? (Are you inflexible and difficult to move?)
- Are the locks broken on your timber box? (Broken boundaries by yourself and by others?)
- Is there a sense of emptiness in your life? (You may have had difficulty holding onto the good things in life).
- On the other hand is this box empty? (You may not have a lot to show for your life i.e. achievements, happy memories, positive learnings, but maybe you did not collect much rubbish on your journey either).
- Is this box full of woodworm? (Is there hurt, anger or resentment eating away at your insides?)
- Is this box cold and damp inside? (No love, joy or fun in your life?)

One day someone may have suggested, that this journey you are on is not a spiritual journey at all. What did you do then? Did you take a good long look at this box "you" and decide to dismantle it, rejecting all that is *yourself*? Did you proceed to hack, chop and saw away at this box? (Did you start intensive work on yourself such as therapies, counselling, self help classes and workshops?)

You must remember this box could be over 40 years old. A sudden onslaught could shatter it to pieces. It could have taken many years for this box "you" to have reached this stage, stuffed to capacity or neglected completely. Do you honestly think that if you dismantle this box, you will be able to move on immediately? You are not going to sort out this box in a few short hours.

Remember it is being with yourself that starts the healing process. It is accepting yourself that allows you to move on. You may need help to sort out the garbage you have collected. You are the box. You can run away from the mess but you cannot run away from yourself. You are still the great being you always were. You (the core being) have not changed.

- You may need help, to discard the contents of this box, which are no longer of any value to you.
- You may need to clean up and repair this box.
- You may need to replace the old screws with new ones (new ideas, new belief systems).
- You may need to repair the lid so that it opens and closes more freely. (Be more flexible with yourself and others and do not restrict yourself or your learnings).
- You may need to fit a new lock on the box so that it is secure. (Create new boundaries for yourself and others).
- You could change the shape and look of this box if you like. (You could begin a new healthy exercise and healthy eating programme).
- You may need to scrape away the layers and layers of paint that are covering up the cracks and woodworm. (Stop covering up dysfunctional or addictive behaviours).
- You may need to learn to deal with your feelings, rather than block them and allow them to build up inside you, i.e. deal with your hurts and angers so that they do not turn to resentments that eat away at your insides. When and if this box is empty, you may need to learn to fill it with all the wonderful gifts life has to offer.
- Most of all you may need to learn to love yourself and see yourself as the great being you truly are.

You may need help from a number of different sources to do all of this. After all many different people created the parts for this box. You got help to be who you are up to this moment with all your discrepancies. You yourself had a part in making this box what it is today, in choosing the carpenters, the tradesmen, (your parents, your family, your friends etc.) You now have a choice what type of carpenters, or trades people will help you repair this box i.e. therapists, family, colleagues and friends.

This box "you" are who you are. You will always be who you are. You can improve and change how you behave. You can change your appearance. You can change how you react and interact with others, but you will always be you, with responsibility only for yourself.

You are the great energy, the great being that has chosen to be here for this learning in this lifetime.

Please do not judge yourself to harshly. You may have been working with the only knowledge you had. You may see your spiritual journey from a different perspective at this point in time. You may like what you have just read and you may not like any of what you have just read, either way it is okay.

If you have learned even one small lesson or made one small discovery about yourself, then this story has been worthwhile. If this has happened, you really are on your spiritual journey.

The only way now is forward.

- Light a candle.
- Sit down and congratulate yourself.
- Ask for help from your guides, your angels, God, to allow you to feel and express your feelings.
- You may need professional help to re-awaken and process old buried memories and feelings. (If we do not feel we cannot heal).

Practice on a daily basis asking yourself the following questions.

- How do I feel?
- Am I tired? What can I do about it? (Give yourself permission to rest).
- Am I unhappy? What is the cause of my unhappiness? (Allow yourself time to answer this honestly and find out what you can do about it).
- Am I sad? (Have you unresolved grief, hurts etc? Allow yourself time for grieving and getting in touch with your hurts. Find out who or what is causing or triggering them).
- Am I angry? What is triggering my anger?
- Do I feel an injustice has been done to me? If so, allow yourself to feel the anger. If an injustice has been done, you are entitled to feel angry.
- Am I feeling guilty about someone, or something I have done? (If this is so, acknowledge your guilt.)

Guilt can be a very controlling emotion. In order to stop guilt controlling you, especially if you did or said something hurtful or harmful through lack of awareness, it is necessary to repeat to yourself and others: "It was the best I could do with the knowledge I had at that time. It is not necessarily what I would do now with the awareness and knowledge I now have."

- Am I fearful? Am I allowing fear to control me?
- Am I feeling helpless and hopeless? Remember you are helpless and hopeless over everyone and everything but yourself. You are never hopeless over yourself. You have everything you will ever need to take you on your journey through life.

Every time you repeat these exercises you further yourself on your spiritual journey. This spiritual journey *is* your life.

Affirmation:

I call on my God, my guides and my angels to support and guide me on my journey.

(19)
The Gold Nugget

The gold nugget is the core You, the perfect You.

Imagine a very dark, deep and murky pond.

There may appear to be very little life in this pond. It may feel for you that life has become stagnant, with very little movement. You may feel that you are unable to move on with your life. It may look as if there has been very little life in this pond for many years.

But there is something amazing at the bottom of this pond (something amazing within you). It is covered in dirt, weeds etc., but it is still perfect. It is still as perfect as the day it was buried there. Here is buried a solid gold nugget.

This is the core You. That perfect being in this dark pond submerged in life. You may not be able to see your way out. You may feel fear at the depths you may have to travel to find that core *you*, – the *you* who became buried and lost many years ago.

All the mud that surrounds you is all the pain, hurts and rejections that life has hurled at you.

You are still perfect. It is that which surrounds you that caused you and others to be blinded to your core being.

Today take time out for You. It is time to rediscover You.

This beautiful gold nugget "*You*" deserves to be brought back into the light. You may have been a baby when you lost sight of "*You*" the real "*You*" but now you are an adult claiming back your true self. That perfect core being is *You*.

You may need help to delve back into the darkness that has surrounded you, but remember that the real you has not gone anywhere.

This sparkling gold nugget (which is *You*) deserves to be cherished. It deserves all the good things that life has to adorn it with. It deserves all the best life has to offer.

- This golden nugget is yours.
- It always was yours.
- It is you.
- It always was you.

Affirmation:

Today is the first day of the rest of my life.

I will do something for myself today – no matter how small.

I will rediscover my core being.

My core being is perfect.

(20)
Impatience

Do you have a sense of impatience with yourself, with other people or with life itself?

Have you felt life has been impatient with you?

Have you felt others have been impatient or intolerant with you and your journey through life?

Are you like the tiny bird that is now afraid to fly because of someone else's impatience?

Has your impatience damaged someone else and inhibited their growth and their ability to fly?

What would you do if you saw a bird's nest with eggs which were almost hatched out? Would you decide it was time the little birds were out, even though you did not know when the eggs were laid? Do you even know what type of bird laid these eggs? Do you know how many leaves, seeds, or how much fruit it will be necessary to have on the trees, to coincide with the birth of the little birds? Do you know what type of weather conditions are most suitable for these particular birds, or what type of food they will need?

When the little birds start to peck their shell to start their journey in life, do *you* decide to speed up this process and break the shell for them? Could it be that these little birds were only checking their strength by pecking their shell? Could it be that they were just preparing for life outside their shell? These little birds knew they would need the strength to be able to break a soft shell, before embarking on their journey and surviving outside in the big harsh world.

If you hasten the chick on his journey you may damage him, and leave him permanently scarred and unable to cope with life. You may physically damage him so that he may never fly. You may mentally damage him by taking away his confidence to do things for himself. You may also create fear in him because he does not know if you are attacking him or trying to help him. All he did was to knock and let you know he was thinking of leaving his safe domain. Did *you* then move in and take control?

How many times after an accident or trauma have you seen a child or an adult moving along at a nice steady pace? You may then decide that it would be better and more beneficial to all, if their rate of recovery could be speeded up. You may do this by encouraging them to try and forget what has happened and move on from their trauma, or you may encourage or sometimes insist on them walking further and faster without their crutches. (These can be emotional or physical crutches). The problem is that you do not really know them, their limits or their capabilities. You may be trying to make them move at the speed *you* think they should be travelling.

Like the chick leaving it's shell, they are moving into new territory and only *they* know when it is safe to move forward and at what speed.

Have you been impatient with your children? Have you wished they would grow and mature faster? Have you tried to pressurise and push them through each stage of their education and development?

Are you impatient with your partner, other family members, employees, friends or work colleagues? Are you impatient in your everyday communication with people you meet e.g. shop keepers, petrol pump attendants, other drivers on the road, someone trying to cross at a pedestrian crossing. Do you show your impatience by beeping your horn, – flashing your lights, – revving your engine and giving hand signals to hurry up? Are you impatient when your food is not ready when you expect it? Do you give curt and short replies to questions you do not have the patience to give full answers to?

Have you been impatient with someone who is sick or injured, continually asking when they will be back at work again? Asking when they will be well enough to finish that job they started for you. This is despite the obvious signs, that they have not fully recovered from their accident or illness? Can you allow them to heal and become healthy again at their own natural speed of recovery? If you insist on them letting go of their crutches before they are ready, they may fall and cause irreparable damage to themselves. They may also lose confidence in their own abilities to act and think for themselves, emotionally, mentally, and physically. These people may be members of your family, your children, your partner or your friends, but you must remember that their pace is not your pace. Their learning is not your learning.

Have you been impatient with others on their journey?

Have you been impatient with yourself on your journey?

You may be an impatient type of person, without being consciously aware of this. But when you do become aware of how your behaviour is affecting yourself and those around you, it is your responsibility whether to continue with this behaviour or not. It is also the responsibility of those around you, whether they allow your impatience to move them at a faster pace than is comfortable or safe for them.

Affirmation:

I will not attempt to hasten the journey of others.

I will learn patience with others.

I will learn patience with myself.

(21)
The Toy

All the talents and all the abilities you will ever need, will come to you naturally and without force.

What happens when you try to force a talent, ability or a situation?

Is life a never-ending struggle for you?

What happens when you do not make use of or misuse the talents and natural abilities you inherit and carry through many incarnations?

Imagine a house with many rooms.

There are many toys in each room.

You are the house. The room is the facility you have to learn and play in. The toys are the talents and abilities you have, to help you learn and deal with relationships, jobs, family and everyday occurrences in life.

See a child who is playing with a toy. This toy is not suitable for this child. It could be too advanced or complicated for him. Eventually he realises this toy will not work the way he wants it to. You see his frustration and offer to help him resolve the problem, but he wants to do it himself. You offer him a more suitable toy, but he rejects it completely. He is hell bent on making this particular toy work. You try to distract him by asking him if he would like to go for a walk with you. He is not interested. He intends to force this toy to work.

He does not see his own limitations or the limits of how much pressure and force this toy will endure. He becomes more and more annoyed, angry and frustrated. He proceeds to bang the toy on the floor. There is the possibility at this point that he is going to break the toy. You tell him to stop, but he does not listen to you. If someone does not remove this toy, he will definitely break it and it will be of no use to him or anyone else.

You now become angry and frustrated with him. Rather than see him completely destroy the toy, you remove it. You know this toy would be more suitable for another child.

This child may have been afraid to let go of the toy in case he did not get another one, or that he would be seen as having failed, because he couldn't make it work. Because of all the frustration and exertion, he is now exhausted and unable to play with another toy. Once the toy has been removed, he may listen to you and your suggestions. He will eventually see that there are many more suitable toys for his particular needs and learnings.

You may persist for years, in trying to force a particular partnership, job or relationship to work, regardless of the numerous signs indicating the amount of damage it is causing to both yourself and others.

It may take you longer to complete certain tasks or jobs. You may feel exhausted when you are finished. You may feel you are unsuited to this particular job, but you have a resistance to letting go of it, in case it would appear you had failed or were not capable of making it work (like it was with the toy).

Like the child you will either break the toy, or someone will take the toy from you. Someone else gets your job, or you may have to give up the job, because of ill health or exhaustion and now you are unable to work. Now you are unable to play with a different toy (job) more suited to your particular talents.

Where a relationship is not working for you, you may become obsessed with making it work. This is not good for you or the other person. You are wasting a valuable lifetime in forcing something to work, which does not come naturally. There is a possibility you may have out-grown the relationship. Outgrown the toy, or the toy was beyond your coping abilities in the first place.

Is it a fear of letting go of the relationship, or of being on your own that forces you to persist? If you do not let go of the relationship, you may lose it anyway. Someone else may arrive on the scene, when they see how you are struggling, and remove your partner (your toy).

What about the things you purchase or attain for yourself, which are not suitable for you? Do you buy unsuitable clothing for yourself and try to make them fit, regardless of the fact that you feel uncomfortable and restricted in them? Do you have unsuitable transport for your particular needs and lifestyle but you insist on making it travel at a speed not recommended for it, or safe for you? Do you overload it beyond its capacity? Do you try to make it what you want it to be, until it eventually breaks down? Now it is of no use to you or anyone else, like the child – you broke the toy.

What about the foods that do not agree with your digestive system? Do you continue to eat it even though your body is rejecting it? Do you take medication to combat the harmful effects of certain foods and drinks on your body? When your system breaks down eventually, do you wonder what has happened to your health? Now you are of little good to yourself or to anyone else.

You may have become so engrossed in making particular toys (talents) work for you, that you have failed to see all the other functional, suitable and appropriate toys (talents), which are readily and easily available to you.

Sometimes what can happen is that some or all of your toys are removed before you can break them. You may have a pre-arrangement with your guides that at a certain stage in your life, they would remove one or all of the toys that were unsuitable for you. Your guides may do this to create space for more suitable toys, so that you can learn from them and enjoy them.

The biggest problem now may be that one or all of your toys may already have been removed or broken, and so you have nothing left. That job you did not change when you had the chance may now have been taken from you. You are now out of work. You had a choice at all times whether to let go of the job voluntarily or not (let go of the toy before you broke it or it was taken from you).

Have you let go now because you have no choice?

- Was your job taken from you and given to someone to whom it was more suitable?
- Maybe you were unable to perform this job as well as was expected or necessary.
- Maybe this job did not suit your particular abilities.
- Maybe your health let you down when you tried to force your body beyond its capabilities.
- Now you cannot work for yourself or anyone else. (You broke yourself and the toy).

The problem may now be that you are without a partner or a job. Someone else may have stepped in and removed your partner, or taken over your job (rescued the toy). This may be a pre-arrangement with your guides to do so, when they could see you could no longer cope with the situation, relationship or job anymore.

Why did you persevere for so long?

Was it a fear of letting go of the relationship? Was it a fear that maybe there would not be another relationship for you (another toy)? Was it because of a fear of failure, that you persisted in trying to make this relationship work, despite the fact that both of you were at breaking point. Have you left this relationship (this toy) broken and beyond repair for yourself or anyone else to enjoy or learn from?

Remember you had free will to voluntarily let go of this relationship (this toy). Sometimes it is only when all our toys (our relationships, worldly possessions, health or job) are taken from us, do we realise we were struggling with something or someone, that was unsuitable for us in the first place.

You may be left in a bare room sitting on the floor. You may now be on your own. You may now realise the toys you were playing with and trying to force to work, were not suitable for you. They were not suitable for your learnings, your growth, your evolvement or your greater good.

Initially when you were forcing these toys to work, it may have appeared they were working for you, but long term and at a deep subconscious level you knew they could never work for you the way you wanted them to. You need to "go with the flow" in order for life to be harmonious and happy.

Try not to spend your life trying to change someone or something to work the way you think it should work. If it does not come naturally you may try to force it. If you force it, you will break it. Learn to know and respect your own limitations, and the limitations of who and what is around you. Do not be afraid to let go of that which may not be suitable for you.

At what point does a child decide a toy is not suitable for him?

The wise child will walk away from this toy and find a more suitable toy. This child does not need to wreck the toy (wreck his health trying to make a toy work that is not suitable for him). The wise adult will also know when it is time to walk away and let go of that job, or relationship etc., or anything else that is unsuitable for him.

Did you ask for God's help?

Sometimes when you ask for God's help his response may not be what you expect it to be. Sometimes God removes the things in life, which are not for our greater good or the greater good of those around us. These are like the toys you are playing with.

You may not be learning from these toys. Forcing your body to work beyond its capabilities is also similar to forcing the toy. The relationships, jobs etc., which you are trying to force to work or will not let go of, despite it being obvious they are not suitable for you, are also the toys you are breaking.

Sometimes you may break the toy and harm yourself in

doing so, or God may remove your toys (relationships, job health and lifestyle) so that you can no longer do yourself or anyone else any more harm.

You may not feel it is for your greater good at this moment in time. *You* may be feeling very annoyed and frustrated, at how God has responded to your cry for help.

Today sit down and ask yourself these questions and answer the questions honestly.

- Am I efforting in my work?
- Am I pushing a work colleague, friend, child, parent or other family member beyond endurance and beyond their capabilities?
- Am I pushing myself beyond my limits and capabilities?
- Am I efforting to make my relationships work?
- Am I trying to force my partner into making our relationship work despite all the obvious signs of incompatibility?
- Am I overloading my physical, emotional and mental bodies and not recognising my limitations?
- Am I exhausted and in ill health with all the pressure I have placed on others and myself?

Affirmation:

I can change me.

I can change my attitudes.

I can learn to let go of that which is unsuitable for me or that which is not for my greater good or for the greater good of all.

I can have a life without efforting.

I can have new learnings (new toys).

**I give myself permission to avail myself
of that which is best suited to me
and for my greater good
and the greater good of all.**

(22)
Overwhelm

Is everything and everyone just too much for you at the moment?

Are you in overwhelm?

Is someone you know in overwhelm or overflow?

Are you unable to take any more?

Is everything too much – even the good things in life?

The symbol of the cup is symbolic of your body.

The symbol of the bin is also symbolic of your body.

Overwhelm is too much of anything, good or bad. When a cup is overflowing it does not matter what caused it to overflow, whether it is good or bad. When it is full to capacity the slightest drop over and above will cause it to overflow.

Your body is similar to that cup. Like the cup, if the physical body has too much food, good or bad, it will overflow. If your emotional body has too much to cope with it, it will overflow or go into overwhelm.

Warnings appear from time to time i.e. physical illness, emotional outbursts, panic attacks and depression. This is your body telling you that it just cannot take anymore.

Overwhelm can occur from too much work, or taking on board too much responsibility, especially that which does not concern you. See the body as a bin. *You* fill the bin to the top, but someone comes along and puts an old newspaper in on top of all your rubbish. The lid blows off the bin (you blow your top). The person who put in the last piece of rubbish gets the blame, but what about all the rubbish you had stored in the bin for all those years?

Do you have a notice on your bin saying, "Dump your rubbish here?" Do you project a message, "Anyone who has a problem – I will solve it?" Do you take other people's issues on board until it all becomes too much for you?

Imagine a day when you were feeling tired. You had a bad night's sleep twisting and turning. You had a list of chores to do in town, so you set off intending to do the minimum. You park your car, but take a chance on not putting a parking ticket on it, as you do not intend to delay very long. You start off walking down the street. First you go to the post office. You forget it is Friday and pension day, so there is a queue a mile long. You eventually go to pay your electricity bill and buy a few light bulbs. After this you go to the bank and find another queue there. You patiently wait but by this time your back is beginning to ache. You go to the local meat store for two lamb chops and some sausages, but having seen some bargains, you decide to buy an extra half dozen items.

Next, you go to the vegetable shop, where of course instead of buying the minimum of vegetables, you decide to buy the full weeks supply. You are already overloaded and the car is at the opposite end of town. As you struggle back to the car you pass the flower shop, and there in the window is a plant that would be lovely on your kitchen window, so you buy this also. You now have about five bags and only two hands.

Where is the joy in all this?

At last you spot the bakery where you usually get a lovely freshly baked apple tart. The trouble is you can barely carry it, but in you go and buy it anyway so you can enjoy a slice with a cup of tea before the kids get home. You are struggling back to your car when your next-door neighbour Sheila sees you. She rushes over to you with a letter saying, "Mary you will be passing a letter box, could you drop this in for me, I'm already late to collect the children from school?" You look at her in horror and think to yourself, "What does she think I am?"

Sheila did not know you were in overflow when she asked you this small favour. You start to cry. Sheila rushes off saying, "I'll do it myself if its too much trouble." This makes you feel even worse. This letter only weighs about 1oz. You will be passing the letterbox, but this small extra task puts you into overflow –"overwhelm." You get to your car only to find you have got a parking fine.

Does any of this sound familiar? On your way home you get delayed by road works and are not home before the kids. They are hungry and looking for their dinner.

Now you are in total overwhelm.

You have a pounding headache. You don't know where to turn. Some survival mechanism might kick in. You eventually feel so ill; you are unable to carry on. Now that you are unwell you feel it is acceptable to ask for help to sort out your shopping and get some rest. You phone your husband, and ask him if he could come home early from work because you feel unwell. When your husband comes home everybody starts fussing and running around you and attempting to help you, but nobody understands your overwhelm. They were not involved in overloading your system – you were. You did not realise your own limitations until it was too late. How long have you been overburdening yourself?

Do you need to get sick in order to learn how *not* to overload your system?

The children looking for their dinner would not cause overwhelm, but that added to all the other events, did. Even if someone made you a cup of tea, the effort of drinking it could be too much for you at this point in time. It can all become too much.

How can you learn?

- By limiting yourself to what you feel capable of doing on certain days.
- Try not to be too judgmental of yourself.

- Ask yourself is there a pattern to your behaviour? If so where did this pattern begin?
- Learn to ask for help.
- Learn to let go of what you do not need.
- Reward yourself on a regular basis – not just when all the chores are finished and the children are tucked up in bed.
- Learn to deal with issues as they happen.
- Learn to create and maintain your boundaries.
- Learn to recognise and accept your limitations.
- Check your "bin" on a regular basis.
- Learn that you can change yourself, but you cannot change anyone else.
- Do not leave yourself available for others to dump their rubbish upon you.
- Learn to love yourself.
- Learn that if you leave your bin at the gate with a sign saying, – "Dump here" – people (including family and friends) are more likely to dump their rubbish in your bin, rather than take their rubbish home with them.

As you learn to take care of yourself, you may find that you are feeling better physically, emotionally and mentally, sleeping well, enjoying life and most of all, are not allowing your bin to become overloaded. It can be beneficial to your physical, emotional and mental health to check your bin on a regular basis, to see how full or how empty it is.

Affirmation:

Today I will check my bin.

I will dump what I do not need.

I will not allow others to dump their rubbish on me.

I will learn to create limits for myself.

I will learn to recognise when I am pushing myself beyond my limits.

I will learn to recognise when I am overloading my physical, emotional and mental system.

I will learn to say "no" to others and myself.

I will learn I do not need to become ill before I can ask for help.

(23)
The Car

Do you have a query about your general health and well-being?

Are you eating the foods best suited to your body's particular needs?

Are you getting sufficient rest?

How many miles have you clocked up on your car (your body)?

The car in this chapter is taken to symbolise the human body. Keeping this image in mind, ask yourself if you have been driving yourself too hard or too fast? Have you been allowing others to drive you too hard? Are you burning yourself out? The red warning light may be flashing for some time, before you become aware of it.

If you were given a car and told it would have to last you ninety years, how would you look after it?

- Would you drive it recklessly or would you drive it with care?
- Would you drive it as fast as you could at every opportunity?
- Would you put a duster over the red warning light, so that you could not see it?
- Would you use second grade petrol or use old oil in the engine?
- Would you leave the engine running when the car had stopped, and never give it a chance to cool down?
- When something went wrong with it, would you ignore

the problem until something more serious went wrong, and only then attend to it?

- Would you allow anybody and everybody to drive it, use it and abuse it?

Do you honestly think this car would last you very long if you continued treating it in this way?

Alternatively, you could make sure that you use the correct oil for the engine, drive it at a comfortable pace, switch off the engine whenever it was not in use and carry out any necessary repairs as soon as they are needed.

Your body is symbolised by the car. Your body must last you a lifetime. If you want it to withstand the rigors of modern living, you must learn how to look after it.

How can this be done?

- By learning *when* to switch off your engine, allowing your body, mind and spirit to cool down and relax.
- By seeking out new ways to improve your life and general well-being.
- By always moving at a pace which is comfortable for your body.
- By taking care to consume only those foods or drinks which agree with your body.
- By not allowing yourself to be pushed faster or harder than is safe or comfortable for you.
- By protecting yourself from people who disregard your feelings and limitations.
- By taking responsibility for your own health and well-being.
- Most importantly by learning how to follow your intuition and gut feelings. In so doing you will instinctively know when to slow down and check your health.

Reflection:

Light a candle for yourself. Breathe deeply and slowly. When you are feeling relaxed, reflect upon the following prayer:

God give me the courage to rest my racing mind and body.

Give me the courage to respect my physical limitations.

Help me to say "no" to others without feeling guilty.

Give me the courage to love and respect myself as I really am.

Give me the courage to ask for help when I need it.

God I thank you for the wonderful gift of life.

Help me to take responsibility for my life and to make the choices in life that are for my greater good and the greater good of all.

Affirmation:

I recognise my need to slow down and relax.

I choose to stay healthy in body, mind and spirit.

(24)
Minimising

Did you ever feel someone was attempting to minimise what was happening for you?

Did you feel angry and annoyed when this happened?

Did someone ever say to you when you complained about something, "Oh come on, it can't be that bad, look at so and so, and how they are and how they cope, they are worse off than you and they are not complaining?"

Have you ever tried minimising what has been happening for someone else by also saying, "It's not that bad, look at so and so, look at how they cope with all their problems?"

Have you yourself or did anyone ever minimise your physical, emotional or mental pain?

Did you ever feel someone was minimising what was happening for you?

Have you ever tried to minimise what was happening for someone else by saying, "It can't be that bad, you're looking fine to me?"

Imagine you are in a restaurant and as you are passing a table, you accidentally lightly hit off the foot of another person. This person reacts very strongly screaming and shouting at you. You are shocked and amazed at the outburst. You say, "I barely touched you." This person is in tears and still very angry. The reaction of this person does not justify what you did, or so you feel. You look at them and say, "Oh for God's sake get a grip on yourself it's not *that* bad, I know I barely touched you!" Yes to a certain extent you are right – what you did was not all *that* bad, but telling this person it is not all that bad is minimising their pain.

What you do not know is that this person had broken their leg some years ago. They have recurring pain since the event and it was necessary for them to undergo surgery in the recent past to reset the broken bone. This person had been out of work for some time, and this night out was a special treat to help cheer them up. As you walked past this person lightly hitting their foot, their body contracted in fear, from the memory of pain from the original injury. This pain may have been reinforced over and over again by other incidences in this person's life. You did not cause their pain to be so severe, but you triggered it. You were responsible for what you did, but not for their reaction to it.

How many times do we minimise emotional pain?

When we see someone crying over what we see to be a minor incident, we may say to him or her "Its not that bad, look at so-and-so and how bad it was for them and they didn't complain or get upset." This is minimising emotional pain. How can any one of us know or begin to know how many hurts or how much pain etc., has been triggered by this (what we are calling a) minor incident?

Sometimes we say or do something that triggers an emotional outburst. Every memory about a similar incident may come to the fore, especially deeply suppressed and painful memories. The outburst, which we sometimes call over-reaction, is like an overflow. The body cannot take any more and it goes into overwhelm. The person experiencing the overwhelm, may not have any insight into why they have over-reacted, or be able to explain it. Deeply suppressed emotional and mental pain needs to be processed and dealt with in order for healing to take place.

If you have experienced or been in the company of someone who you may feel is over-reacting, try not to judge them too harshly. You too may have suppressed some painful memories along the road you have travelled. Other people may trigger your hurt or pain from time to time and you may react in the only way you know how. We do not suppress happy memories – only painful ones.

No therapy can change what has happened, but it can decrease the intensity of the incident, leaving it a memory, rather than a crippling emotion. Help is available in the form of counselling, therapy and support groups.

The next time you see someone, who is, in your opinion over-reacting, pause for a moment:

- Take a deep breath
- Try not to minimise their pain.
- Try not to be judgemental of their reaction or their behaviour.
- You do not know the road they have travelled or the journey they may be about to travel.

You may also need to seek professional help in order to get in touch with any painful memories, wounds and hurts you may have experienced and suppressed, so that they can be dealt with and healed.

Affirmation:

I will not minimise my own pain.

I will not minimise the pain of another person.

(25)
The Football Game

Do you have a tendency to get involved in other people's games (other people's issues)?

Do you sometimes become involved without being invited to join in?

Do you have difficulty being a spectator, when other people are having problems in their lives?

Do you sometimes believe that you know best, when it comes to resolving other people's problems?

Do you have a tendency to leave your own space, when you see issues that you do not agree with or sometimes do not even concern you?

Imagine you go to a football match, just as a spectator. See yourself standing on the sideline observing the game. You know a little about the game, the rules and some of the tactics of certain players. From where you stand you can see that certain players are cheating and are not playing a fair game. You have already decided which team should win, not because of their abilities, but because of your own personal choice and your belief system.

Remember you are still just an observer, but *you* decide the referee is not treating your favourite team fairly. (Now you have started to take sides).

Now (in your head) you have become the referee. *You* are deciding what he should do and not do. All of a sudden (in your head) you are on the pitch in the middle of the game trying to interfere in the referees decision. Now that you are in the middle of the pitch, you cannot see the game clearly.

How do you get out of this situation?

Ask yourself, what brought you into this game in the first place?

- Do you have issues of your own that you are avoiding and need to deal with?
- Are you using this game to distract you from these issues?

You do not know the rules of other people's games. You do not know the full history of their past. How can they play out their game with an extra player on the pitch, a player who does *not know* the score, is not impartial, and is making judgments? They cannot learn and neither can you. Have you left your space? Have you been trying to be all things to all men?

How many times have *you* tried to interfere in a family or a friend's situation, offering advice and making suggestions, (which you were not asked for), on how *they* should live their lives? You do not know their full capabilities or lack of them (here you are back on the football field). This is your interpretation of their game. You were only a spectator, but you decided to be a player on someone else's pitch.

Did someone ask you to play in the game or merely ask you a question about the game? When did you suddenly become an authority? What gives you the right, to impose or try to enforce your beliefs or opinions on other people?

How can they learn if you are on their pitch scoring, pushing, playing and making decisions for and against them? How can your family or friends learn about life, if you try to live their lives for them?

Get off this pitch.

It is not yours. Look at your own pitch and your own game. Create your own rules. Put up your own goal posts. Pick your own team. Play with the team that will provide the best learnings for *you*.

Your interference may have affected the flow of other people's learnings and put *your* learnings on hold.

Can you afford to put your learnings on hold? You left your space. Someone else could now be filling it. You left your space and became the linesman, the referee and the players. Eventually exhausted, overwhelmed and unwell you quit.

The game of life goes on with or without us. How we participate is our own choice. We can be beside, behind, beyond, below or above another human being – but we can never ever "be" for them.

The next time you find yourself becoming involved in someone else's game (someone else's issues) without being invited to join in, take a deep breath and ask yourself:

- What are your real reasons for getting involved in this game?
- Does it allow you to forget your own problems for a while?
- Does it make you feel good?
- Are you helping or enabling or trying to fix?
- Is there a pattern to your behaviour?

The law of the universe is non-interference:
Do not cross the road and tell someone what you think.
Give your opinion if and only when you are asked for your point of view.

Affirmation:

I will learn to stand back from other people's games, (other people's issues).

If I am asked to join in I will make a decision whether to join in or not, depending on whether it is for my greater good or the greater good of all.

(26)
Inner Forgiveness

Do you have a problem with forgiveness?

Do you have difficulty forgiving yourself?

Do you have difficulty forgiving others?

To forgive oneself, is probably one of the most difficult tasks we may ever have to accomplish. One possible reason for this could be that we ourselves may not have a limit, on when we have been punished enough, for some misdeed we feel we may have committed. It would therefore be very difficult for us to know when someone else has been punished enough for a misdeed.

When you become aware that everything you do has a knock-on effect, you may become more aware of your every action, and the possible consequences. You are responsible for every action you take. Every action you take creates a reaction.

When you play a part in an event such as a major accident where another person dies, is maimed or injured you may experience feelings of guilt. You may need to acknowledge what part of this accident you are responsible for. You may also need to acknowledge any feelings of guilt you may be experiencing, as a result of this accident. What is also important is that you do not allow the guilt to control your life, or that you do not try to take responsibility for the total event. You do not have a right to try to take responsibility for the behaviour and actions of others. That is their experience and their learning.

You can play a part in someone's life but you can never be all of their life, or take responsibility for it.

Take for example an accident such as a fire, where there are four people involved. One person dies as a result of their injuries, another person is seriously injured and the other two have slight injuries.

Without any prior arrangements, these four people meet at a certain place and time. The events that follow, change the course of their lives and the lives of those around them forever. An accident happens because of a sequence of events, which no one person has total control over. Each person must take full responsibility for the individual part they played in the event that followed their meeting. No one person is responsible for the actions or reactions of the other people involved. Every action creates a reaction. For example if either person A, B, C, or D, stayed at home on the night in question, the outcome of the night would not be the same. There are no "ifs." What happened, happened and can only be dealt with and healed from, but it can never be changed.

As a result of this accident one person dies and leaves behind anguish, hurt, anger and guilt. The three who survive must then come to terms with what has happened. They cannot change it. Each individual may need to put the part they played in the event into perspective in relation to the total event. The person, who is most seriously injured, may feel he himself is guilty and responsible for the total event, because of *his* actions, even though in reality he is only responsible for the part *he* played.

All three survivors may individually feel responsible for the person who has died. They may individually feel guilty, because they survived and he did not. One of the least injured may feel guilty for the part he played and for not being able to do more, to prevent the final outcome. This man must realise he is responsible only for the part he played, and cannot take responsibility for the parts played by the other three people, for how they reacted, or for the final outcome.

The situation worsened, because of a sequence of events causing electrical failure, which suddenly left the premises in total darkness. Each person reacted in the only way they knew how. One individual (reacting faster than the others) found himself in a situation where he must make a frantic decision. (a) To return to the place from where he had earlier escaped death and rescue his three friends, or (b) escape himself. He chose the former, with little or no regard for his own health or safety.

He is not responsible for where they were on the night in question or where they are today.

He is not responsible for the part they played in the event.

He *is* responsible for *his* part of the total event, but he is *not responsible* for *all* of the event, or the outcome following the event.

He saved the lives of three people at the time. The fact that one of these people died at a later stage, is not his responsibility. He is responsible for saving the lives of three people, what happens after that is out of his control.

Despite the enormity of what this person has achieved in rescuing these people, he may find at a later stage, he is overwhelmed with guilt and remorse, because of the part he played in the events leading up to the final traumatic results.

He is responsible for his own acts and deeds, but he is not responsible for other people's reactions. Their reaction is based on the learnings and experiences they have already had and how they coped with situations in the past.

If a number of people are involved in a trauma, or accident, each time they meet up following the event, they may trigger hurt, pain, sadness, anger or guilt for each other. Sometimes the guilt or emotion for one person can become so enormous, it can affect and control them for the rest of their lives. They can become so controlled by this guilt, that guilt becomes their reality. They may find that they will continually find themselves in situations of shame and guilt. They may create situations where they will experience blame and rejection.

Feelings of guilt, and not deserving, can be a factor in preventing this person's life from becoming harmonious and happy, when he experiences feelings of guilt and not deserving. He is back on familiar ground again i.e. "I don't deserve", "I am a bad person".

Logic will tell him he is not guilty for the total incident, but his feeling of guilt will continue to control his life until he acknowledges the feeling, and acknowledges the part he played. He must learn he is only responsible for his part. He must learn and understand, that he cannot take responsibility for the actions or reactions of others.

How does a person who is overwhelmed with guilt move on with their lives and stop allowing guilt to control them? The punishment this person is inflicting on himself, may be far greater than the crime he believes he has committed.

This person may need to separate the person they are now from their behaviour. If at the time of an incident they felt what they were doing was not wrong or harmful, then they are not guilty. This person may need to learn inner forgiveness.

To release yourself from guilt you need first to acknowledge your guilt. You need to learn to say to yourself:

- I DID THE BEST I COULD.
- I had no preconceived idea of the possible outcome of my actions.
- I worked and acted with the knowledge I had at the time.
- I played a part in an incident, that was neither preordained nor premeditated, which ended in tragedy.
- I acknowledge that my actions and reactions, together with the actions and reactions of others, resulted in an outcome that were far reaching and beyond comprehension and logic.
- My actions and reactions were based on what was happening at the time.

- How can I begin to forgive others, if I cannot forgive myself?

People, who have had this type or similar types of experiences, may need professional help to process and heal from what has happened.

Affirmation:

I separate my behaviour from me the person I am.

I ask God to forgive me, for any part I may have inadvertently played in an incident, where another person was harmed or injured.

I am a good and caring person.

I ask forgiveness for any past misdeeds, which I may have carried out.

I thank God for the awareness I now have.

I cannot forgive others, until I learn inner forgiveness.

I will learn inner forgiveness.

In learning to forgive myself, I will learn to forgive others.

(27)
The Hub Of The Wheel

What part are you playing in another person's life? What part are you playing in the life of your partner, family or friends?

You are the hub of the wheel.

You are the hub of your own wheel. (You are the centre or core of your own life). You may have spent time believing you could be the hub in someone else's wheel, (the centre of someone else's life). You can never be the hub of someone else's wheel. This can never be. You can however be a minor or a major spoke in someone else's wheel and they in yours, but you will never be their hub.

You need to be in a good state of repair to keep your wheel turning. (You need to be in good health physically, emotionally and mentally to live life to the full).

Each hub needs four main spokes to keep the wheel balanced. These are the aspects of your life that support you, keep you balanced and help you to survive and live a healthy life.

The four main spokes (aspects) are:

- Healthy living conditions.
- Fresh air and sunshine.
- Good food.
- Love.

This wheel can have many smaller spokes. The smaller spokes are the people and happenings that play a minor part in your life. The rim of the wheel is what holds the minor and major spokes together, (the minor and major aspects of your life). The rim also keeps all the spokes connected to the hub (you).

If the rim is a bit battered, a bit shaky, a bit thin or worn out, it may have difficulty holding all the aspects of your life together, or keeping the hub (you) connected to those aspects i.e. family, friends, life in general. (If you have put too much pressure on your health, family and friends they may be feeling a bit worn out, and they may have become disconnected from you).

If the hub is battered and out of shape, or if it has been pressurised and forced to facilitate uneven or damaged spokes, it cannot keep the wheel balanced. (If you have tried to adjust or change your life, your beliefs or your space continually to facilitate other people, you will be out of balance and out of sync. It could be difficult for you to hold on to what is necessary, for you to survive in life.

If one of your main spokes is damaged (an aspect of your health), or if one of your main spokes is too lose (you do not have enough limitations in your life or on yourself), or if one of your spokes is out of line (you do not have a sense of direction in life), then either of these spokes will eventually knock the other spokes out of balance.

The hub (you) could survive on three spokes for a time. You could survive with three good spokes and one damaged spoke (minor ailment). The problem is the longer the damaged spoke is left without being mended, the more pressure this will put on the other three spokes, and on the rim of the wheel. Eventually you may lose another spoke (another of the necessary resources for a healthy life). When the pressure is put on your wheel it is likely to collapse at the place where the weakest and most damaged or missing spokes are. Your wheel will not turn on just two spokes.

It is possible that all of your four main spokes are slightly damaged. (There may be many aspects of your life that need to be tended to). These spokes are but aspects of your life. They are not your life. If the hub is in a good state of repair (if you have taken good care of yourself physically, emotionally and mentally over the years) and it then happens that your spokes and rim deteriorate, you can repair the damage or replace them. On the other hand if your hub has been allowed to get into a serious state of disrepair, it will not hold the other aspects of your life together.

You must first look at the hub (you). If there are changes to be made regarding your health or your life, you must first make these changes within yourself.

You may need to check your hub (get a good general check-up on yourself, body, mind and spirit).

- Check your health and your general well-being. Check that the spokes you have in your hub are best suited to your particular hub.
- Check that you are experiencing joy, love, sharing, and learning with the people who share your life.
- Check that the foods you eat are the best you can obtain for your particular system.
- Check that the source and amount of fresh air and sunshine you may be receiving, are what is sufficient and best for you.
- Check that your living conditions are healthy and are a source of comfort and enjoyment for you.
- When you take care of the hub (you) you can show others by example how they can take care of themselves.
- You can learn how not to allow too much pressure to be put on the hub (you).
- You can learn not to adjust your hub every time you encounter a spoke that does not fit.
- You can learn not to try and facilitate everyone and every situation you encounter in life.

- You can learn to compromise in a situation, but not to compromise yourself.
- If you keep the hub (you) and wheel (aspects of your life) balanced and in good working order you may share a life with or encounter another likeminded wheel (like-minded person). You could together support a cart (another way of being) that could take you on a journey of peace, harmony and happiness.

Affirmation:

I will check my hub (my life) today.

I will repair or replace any damaged spokes (any people or issues in my life) that are affecting my hub.

I will strengthen and repair the rim of my wheel.

I will resolve, heal and deal with issues, which are affecting my life and myself.

(28)
Blame

Do you have a tendency to blame?

Is it everybody's fault but yours when something goes wrong?

When you blame you become powerless. You give away your power to others, to hurt or affect you in some way.

If you say, "***You*** made me angry when you borrowed my car without asking," – you are now blaming.

If you say, "***I feel*** really angry because you borrowed my car without asking," – you are now dealing with your feelings. You are expressing how *you feel* and in doing so, you are empowering yourself.

The other person may retort by saying, "I did not mean to upset you or make you angry."

You can reply by saying, "I did not say you meant it, but I am saying how *I* feel about the incident."

Saying the words "I feel" is self-empowering.

By saying "I feel" – you are not resorting to blaming others.

(29)
The Spring

Are you wound up like a spring?

Do you feel uptight?

This story is about life. It is about how our bodies and our minds can be wound up like a spring that is about to snap.

- Do you feel wound up like a spring? (Do you feel wound up today)?
- Do you feel your spring is on the verge of breaking? (Are you on the verge of breaking down)?
- Is your spring so tight it could snap at any time? (Are you so uptight you could snap at any time)?
- Are you allowing family members, friends or work colleagues, "to wind up" your spring?
- Are you, yourself winding up your spring, not knowing any other way of being? This could be either from habit or conditioning.
- Are your muscles tight?
- Are you ready to take flight at a moments notice?
- Are you walking on a path you do not see?
- Are you breathing in air you do not feel?
- Is there a frown on your forehead, from trying to figure out your life and the lives of those around you?
- Are you looking with unseeing eyes?
- Are your ears blocked with words and noise you do not wish to hear anymore?

- Are you listening without hearing?
- Are your fists constantly clenched, afraid of letting go?
- Is there a knot in your gut like a coil?
- When you try to sleep does your mind continue to race away?

You may be feeling you can no longer slow down your thoughts or switch them off. Is your mind so full of thoughts and emotions, you cannot think straight anymore? Do you find when you are about to relax or unwind, something happens to wind you up again? Do you feel that you never really get to the point of relaxation, where you feel totally unwound? Do you have a belief system that if you relax something will go wrong?

The question is where did all of this begin?

It could have been as a result of a fall or trauma your mother experienced prior to your birth. As your mother's body contracted to protect itself, the baby's body could have absorbed the shock and also contracted to protect itself. In doing so, it could have started a lifetime of tension and a fear of letting go. A fear of relaxing.

It could have started for you in early childhood, where you were involved in an accident or trauma. This could have been reinforced by life's experiences, where you learned it is not safe to let go. "It is not safe to relax. You are not good enough if you cannot keep going indefinitely, regardless of how you feel. If you are resting you are lazy. Don't stop. Keep going at all costs or something will go wrong."

Where did you first hear these messages?

Did you have a lifetime of constant tension – school, parents, work etc., which reinforced your belief systems? "You cannot relax, you cannot sit down."

- Did you choose situations, jobs or relationships, which triggered and reinforced your tension – this being the only reality you knew?

- Do you now have high expectations of yourself?
- Do others have high expectations of you also?

Today, look at this spring. This is you. You may feel so tightly wound up, you can hardly breathe. You may be afraid to let go in case you fall apart. Can you see any resemblance to your life in this story? If so what are you going to do about it? Do you want to do something about it? If the answer is "yes" take time out to look at where you are at in life. Look at how life is for you at this moment in time. What can you do to change it? You could release this spring suddenly, (bring yourself to a sudden and complete halt). By doing this you could damage all the small wheels and cogs that keep you going. A better course of action could be:

- Stop winding up your spring.
- Stop allowing others to wind up your spring.
- Try and find out where it all began (when you find the cause you are halfway to the cure).
- You may need professional help to retrace your steps and learn new life coping skills.
- Learn to become aware of the holding patterns in your body.
- Learn where, when, and how you hold tension in your body.
- Learn to respond rather than react.
- Learn to deal with stressful situations at the time they happen rather than internalising them, taking them on board, and carrying them around with you.
- Learn you are not responsible for anyone but yourself.
- Learn to offload that which does not belong to you (other people's rubbish, other people's issues).
- Learn relaxation techniques i.e. meditation, yoga or breathing exercises.

- Give yourself permission to take time out and relax.
- Take up a sport or activity you enjoy, rather than one you have to work at.
- Be aware of the air you breathe, the sounds you hear and the sounds of nature.

Try not to be too critical of yourself. It may have taken you most of your life to get your spring to where it is at this moment in time but it will not take a lifetime to unwind it.

Start today.

Today can be the first day of the rest of your life.

Affirmation:

I will stop winding up my spring

I will stop allowing others to wind my spring.

I will get help to unwind my spring.

I will be patient with myself, and reward myself with each positive change I make – no matter how small.

(30)
Pain

Do you feel pain, (Physical, emotional or mental)?

If you are feeling pain, physical, emotional or mental, it may be time to look at the cause. Pain is the body's warning system that something is wrong. If you continually block pain by taking painkillers, alcohol or anti-depressants the body may become severely damaged.

Is your pain being triggered and reinforced?

Feelings of pain can be blocked out from past life traumas, early childhood and present day traumas. Where there is severe shock or trauma, we shut down in order to heal. The physical body will bleed, form a scab and eventually heal. We would not, however, put a plaster on the wound at the time of the injury and leave it for twenty or thirty years before we would look at it again. If we did this, the entire area around the wound would have become infected.

This is what can happen to the emotional and mental bodies. We may close down and suppress the feelings, which are associated with whatever traumas that have affected us. This can be a temporary shut down in order to heal, but for many it can be a lifetime of suppressed emotions and feelings. We shut down on the feelings of pain, shock and trauma in order to heal, but the fear is, if we get in touch with the feelings, we will experience all the original pain, shock and trauma again. We must remember we can never again experience the exact same pain associated with a particular incident, even if we wanted to. We may have similar experiences that trigger a memory, but never the same experience or pain. Remember, it may have been you as a child who suppressed the memory, but it is you as an adult who is now dealing with and trying to heal from it.

Let us assume for example, you had a car accident as a young child. You would have experienced the physical pain of the injuries. The emotional pain may be the fear you may now be experiencing. You may have fear of travelling or fear of speed. The physical body may have healed, but each time you sit into a car, the fear is triggered. The physical body contracts to protect itself, and in doing so squeezes down on the physical injury and triggers the pain.

Emotional pain without physical pain.

You may at some time in your life have experienced the loss of a loved one, through accident or illness. Some time later you may attend the funeral of a relative or friend or of a person unknown to you, the sorrow and grief being experienced and expressed by those around you, may trigger your own loss. You shed tears of sadness, not for those around you but for your own loss. This is called the trigger situation. You can experience feelings of sadness, loss, grief or anger, associated with your own memory, but you can never have the actual experience again, even if you wanted to.

Another example is, if a child stays out later than the permitted time and does not phone home. The parents will become anxious and concerned once a certain length of time has passed beyond the permitted time. As more time passes and there is no phone call from their child, anxiety will turn to fear. If from the past, the parents have a memory of loss of a child, relative or friend, the fear will be much greater. The pain of the loss is now triggered and the body contracts to prepare itself for the possibility of bad news.

Suddenly the child arrives home, totally unaware of the anxiety and concern they have caused the parents. The parents may first feel relief, which can then turn to anger because their child has unwittingly triggered the memory of their trauma from the past, from which they have not yet fully healed.

Painful memories of an incident can be stuck in the subconscious mind. The memories can be triggered when a similar incident occurs. Emotional, mental and physical trauma is best dealt with as and when it happens. This prevents the sometimes crippling after affects. No therapy can change what has happened in a person's life, but it can decrease the intensity of the incident, allowing it to become a memory, rather than a crippling emotion.

Affirmation:

I ask my God, my guides, my angels to help me deal with, and heal from, any old memories, wounds, or hurts that I may have suppressed.

(31)
The Journey

Are you wondering why everyone appears to be so different from you?

Their learning is also different from yours.

Your learnings may be similar to that of another person but they will never be the same.

You are unique.

On the journey through life people often stop to look for meaning and perspective. The lesson that this chapter seeks to teach, is that it is not the length of time spent on this earth that matters, but the way you use the time you have been given. It is the *how* rather than *how long* that is significant in terms of how you live. It is the learnings you have on your journey and *how you apply* those learnings, which ultimately make you the person you are today, and the person you would like to become. Your learnings may be similar to that of another person, but they will never be the same.

Continuing with the analogy of life as a journey let us look at the journeys of four people who all decided to travel from point "A," to their destination at point "B," a total distance of eighty miles.

Imagine the car as your body.

When you reach the final destination, you leave your physical body and move back into spirit.

We will start with Tom.

Tom got a fast car and completed his journey in a very short time. Obviously he did not have much to learn on the way, except to experience some minor learnings, and create learning opportunities for the people who came into contact with him on his journey. Tom then returned back into spirit at a young age. Tom had many previous lifetimes where he availed of many of life's learning experiences and had little to learn this time around.

Next we have Mary.

Mary may choose an old banger of a car that may take many days for the journey from "A" to "B." She may spend most of the journey broken down on the roadside or in the garage. She may also have broken windscreen wipers and cannot see where she is going most of the time. She will eventually reach her destination (after a long life with poor vision and minor illnesses).

Now Joe.

Joe may choose a fairly good car and travel the scenic route (he observes all that is happening around him). Joe is the person who moves through life at a nice steady pace. He does not over-do anything and he lives to a ripe old age.

Finally Sam's story.

Sam gets a fairly good car but on Sam's journey he decides to pick up every traveller that he passes on the road. In life he takes on relatives and friends (passengers) and tries to live their lives for them. He sees little and learns less. His whole journey is spent making decisions, always with others in mind. They learn little or nothing, because Sam takes full responsibility for them, for their food, their enjoyment, their health, their behaviour, and for their well-being.

Sam does not notice that his car is over-burdened. His engine is burning out and his tyres are bald. He travels the last part of his journey in misery. He has also become irritable and less tolerant with his passengers. He does not want to stop and leave them on the side of the road, because they may not know their way. They are angry because he led them to believe he would take them the full journey. Sam's car does not make the full journey. (Sam becomes ill). So his passengers have to get out and walk. Sam's passengers now have to take care of themselves, their lives and their health.

The problem now is that these people have not walked from the time they first met Sam. (They never learned to take responsibility for their own lives). How can they start now? Sam moves back into spirit leaving behind him some very angry people. Sam did not learn in this lifetime and neither did his passengers.

Are you learning in this lifetime?

- Ask yourself, is there something *you* need to learn about yourself, your journey or your fellow travellers?
- What stage are *you* at on your journey?
- Are you content and happy on your journey or are you overloaded and over burdened?
- Are you denying others, their learnings by taking them and their issues on board, and not allowing them to learn for themselves?

It is not the length of the journey that is important but what we learn on the journey.

Affirmation:

I can make changes on my journey for my greater good and the greater good of all.

This is my journey and mine alone.

I am not responsible for anyone else's journey.

I can help my fellow travellers but I do not need to take them on board.

(32)
Dumping Rubbish

Do you project a message to others "Dump here?"

- Are you feeling overburdened?
- Do you feel laden down with other people's problems and their unresolved issues?
- Do you have any awareness or insight into what is the cause of those feelings?
- Is your own behaviour contributing in any way to your feelings of being overburdened?
- Are you taking issues on board that are not yours to resolve?
- Are you feeling guilty or inadequate when you are unable to resolve the physical, emotional and financial problems of your family or friends?

It may be time now to take a long look at your own behaviour and what you are projecting. It may also be time to take a look at your family and friends, and see how they are reacting to your behaviour and the messages you are relaying to them.

In the course of our daily lives we may collect garbage both physical and emotional. Most of this does not really belong to us. Conditioning however says that we must hold on to it, and as time passes by, we may forget where it came from or how we can discard it. Our bodies and our minds may eventually get tired of the burden. All the old angers, hurts and injustices become piled up one on top of the other, and what started out as a small hurt, can become a major issue.

For example if you throw potato skins (which were once

quite edible) into the dustbin and then pile in a load of rubbish on top of the skins, all of this waste food eventually becomes rotten. If you do not deal with minor issues as they happen and then allow more serious issues to be piled on top of them, all of the issues added together over a period of time can become a serious problem.

Anger is an emotion, which can be very close to the surface. A seemingly minor incident could cause an angry reaction. How do we know how many other major and minor incidences that may be buried deep in the body and suppressed for many years? When the bin (the body) becomes overloaded and overburdened, it begins to overflow.

Let us say that your next-door neighbour arrives at your house one day with a large plastic bag full of rubbish, and dumps the contents on the middle of your kitchen floor. Would you tell him that his behaviour is quite acceptable, and that you will sort out all his rubbish for him? Are you more likely to get really annoyed and tell him in no uncertain terms how you *feel*, and tell him to pick up his rubbish and dump it elsewhere? Your reaction would most likely be the latter.

Why then do you allow emotional and mental rubbish to be dumped on you by family members, relatives and friends? Is it because you are conditioned to believe that you must not just "listen" to other people's problems but that you must actually take them on board and sort out their problems (their rubbish) for them? You must learn that other people's problems are not yours, and you do not have the right to take on board or try to sort out other people's rubbish.

Whilst problems are far from enjoyable experiences, they may be "set up" at another level to provide a learning experience for us. So when you take someone else's problem on board and attempt to solve it, or sort it out for them, you are depriving them of their own personal learning experience.

How can they learn from it? Regardless of the problem or situation, it is still their problem and in dealing with it their way, it becomes yet another valuable learning experience for them.

You have free will at all times which allows you to decide one of the following:

(a). Do you allow others to sort out their own problems, or

(b) Do you take their problems on board (their rubbish) and try to sort it out for them?

If you are asked for help, you can decide whether to help or not. After all it is *their* problem, *their* rubbish. They collected it. Their learning is in sorting it all out. None of us have the right to attempt to deprive another person of their learnings.

Ask yourself, are you allowing others to dump their physical, emotional or mental rubbish on you?

Ask for help to learn how to say "no."

Affirmation:

I change my sign to:

"Dumping of rubbish is NOT PERMITTED

here anymore."

(33)
The Walls Of The House

The house in this story is what two people have created. Each end wall of the house is each person in the relationship. The roof is what ties the two people together.

You may be playing the part of either of the two people in this story. Neither of these people are right or wrong. It is where they are at in life's journey that is important. If you are the wall that collapses, it is okay. If you are the wall that stays standing that is also okay.

There are two opposite end walls on a house. One end wall we could call the husband and the other one is the wife. What joins them together is the roof, (the relationship between the two).

Take a situation where the roof is a bit shaky. There may be a lot of pressure on the roof, financial, work related or family pressures.

Supposing now that there is more pressure on one end of the roof than the other. Inevitably this end is more likely to collapse, bringing with it the wall directly underneath.

For the purpose of identification we will see the left wall as the husband and the right one as the wife.

Take the left end wall of the house: The husband.

The left wall was built by good block layers, (parents) on a good foundation, up as far as row ten. The block layers mixed the cement to the right consistency and built every block carefully up as far as the tenth row of blocks. (This husband was cared for and well looked after until he was ten years of age). Then the block layers (parents) go away for a day and another block layer comes in to replace them (a babysitter).

The behaviour of this new block layer was not appropriate. He laid a row of blocks that were "out of line." They were well camouflaged and were not noticed by anybody. (He abused and crossed boundaries that were not his to cross).

The parents of this boy return from their trip and everything appears to be normal on the surface. Their son's behaviour is out of character, but they put this down to insecurity because of their brief absence. The parents take over again restructuring and trying to build on this row of shaky blocks. It is not clear to the visible eye what the matter is with the ten-year-old boy, and as time goes on the badly built layer of blocks become hidden away beneath the other blocks. Apart from a rather vague memory of something happening to him around the age of ten, he feels fine. After going through the various ups and downs of teenage life, this boy reached adulthood. He experienced many different and difficult relationships, but still did not manage to have a close relationship with anybody.

The other end wall of the house: The wife.

This mans wife from the age of one was constantly moved from one childminder to another. Her parents put in a good foundation, but after the first row of blocks they decided to subcontract the rest of the work to different block layers. (Many different people took care of this child). Every other row was different. There was no consistency anywhere.

Eventually the wall was built as far as the second floor, (approximately row fourteen). At this point her parents decided to take over the job again. They realised that they should have been there for her in her formative years, but they did the best they could. They just "plastered up" the uneven surfaces built by the various subcontracted block layers, and made the wall look good to the visible eye (good schools, good education, good clothes, good living conditions etc).

This girl left school with fairly good results and got herself a job. However, she was always a bit of a drifter. She never felt settled anywhere for any length of time. After a certain period of time she would sense rejection and could leave her job or home at a moments notice (this wall could move at any time).

Eventually this man and woman meet and decide to marry. Both may have a slight awareness of their individual weaknesses (i.e. damaged walls). They feel if there is something holding the walls together and preventing them from falling, in this case a roof, (a marriage) then the walls may not fall. One person does not know where the flaws are in the other person's walls, and so they erect a roof (they get married).

Shortly after the marriage this man's wife realises her husband has major issues around trust. As the years pass these problems become more obvious and difficult to deal with. He refuses to allow his children to be left alone with anybody for reasons even he cannot explain. He will not allow his older children to go out on their own and they feel he is stifling their lives. He and his wife have many arguments over all of this. He says he does not know why he has a problem trusting anybody, and she claims that he just does not want to tell her. She suspects something may have happened to him in early childhood, which may have caused his inability to trust.

The pressures then start with friends, in-laws, business and financial problems. Addictive or dysfunctional behaviour may also cause added pressures on the marriage. Engaging in this type of behaviour can be denial that there is a problem in the marriage, or it could be a learned coping mechanism from the past.

Because of the fact that core issues and traumas were not dealt with and resolved before marriage, or in the early stages when it was obvious there were problems, the marriage may now be in jeopardy. As time passes and no resolution to the core issues have been discovered or resolved, the ability to communicate and relate to each other may now be more difficult. Old angers from the past, and resentments towards each other, may now be triggered at this point.

After years of trying to hold the marriage together, this woman decides she needs help to prevent *her* wall from falling. With the aid of therapists and counsellors she pulls off all the old plaster. She seeks help to find out where the initial damage was done. She begins to see where it all went wrong. She realises that those early years had many faults, and painful as they were, she is nonetheless prepared to look at the past and deal with it.

She is now fully aware of all the assistance available to her such as counselling, books on self-development and many different types of therapies. She avails of the support available to her. She becomes more positive. (She is now better able to shoulder the weight of the roof). She has found her strength by having found the source of her problems. Some of these problems may have been caused by the people she depended on and trusted in her early years.

In the meantime, what is happening to the other wall?

This woman's husband cannot understand why there is a bulge at row ten on his wall. He does not know what to do about it. The more his wife's wall straightens up, the more pressure there seems to be on his wall.

This man may be in denial or may have difficulty accepting that his own basic structure is unsound. He may have blocked painful memories at a subconscious level.

One day the roof collapses altogether. (The marriage falls apart).

This man does not know where to start looking for help. Fear of uncovering something from his early childhood may be preventing him from seeking the help available to him. For a time this man feels hopeless and depressed. He knows he needs help. He must find the cause of *his* damaged wall in order to rebuild *his* life.

What can he do under these circumstances?

Sometimes if the walls are severely damaged, it may be necessary to go back as far as that shaky row, and build again from there. He does not have to do it all himself this time. He can get professional help and follow the example set by his wife. He can observe the way she resolved and dealt with the problems in her wall. With help he can build up his own rows of blocks this time, using the many good blocks available to him (the many goods things that have happened in his life). With help he can rebuild his wall again, this time making it strong and secure.

How are *your* walls?

Do you have any "blocks" in any rows (years) that are "out of line," which may need to be straightened and dealt with? Have you had traumas, accidents or incidents in your life, which may be causing you to feel "shaky" at this moment in time?

For a roof to be properly supported, both walls need to be secure, safe, strong, level and solid. These walls will last longer and withstand more pressure if they have no weak, uneven or out of line blocks in them, particularly in the lower rows (early years).

You may need to throw away or sort out damaged shaky blocks and replace them with new ones. Taking positive action, allowing in new ideas, new belief systems and availing of therapies, can be of help to do all of this.

When difficult issues and weaknesses of any kind in the structure have been dealt with, this wall can then support itself. It can also stand beside another similarly strengthened wall and support any weight.

After it has been repaired, this wall can decide to continue supporting the old roof, or it may decide to stand beside a new wall and share a completely new roof.

Affirmation:

I will look at the walls in my house.

If there are weak spots I will acknowledge and strengthen them.

If there are blocks or rows of blocks out of alignment I will straighten them.

If there are issues in my life that need to be resolved I will resolve them. If I need help to resolve my issues I will seek help.

(34)
Hoarding

Are you a hoarder?

Do you have a problem letting go?

Do you have a problem creating space in your life for new ideas, new people and new relationships?

Are you stopping the natural flow of universal energy?

Are you like the ship that is stuck in the dock, where one ship cannot get out, and the other ships cannot get in?

Do you block or impede the natural flow of universal energy by hoarding?

You could be doing this unknowingly, by holding on to goods such as items of clothing, old books, or household items, which you may have outgrown and may no longer have any use for.

You could move these items on, by taking them to your local charity shop or jumble sale.

You could even pass them on to a friend or neighbour, who could have some use for them.

You could also be blocking the natural flow of energy by holding on to a relationship, which you both may have outgrown.

Without being consciously aware of it you may be blocking and impeding family, friends, workmates, employees or employers on their journey, by not allowing *them* to move on.

Affirmation:

Today I will do a stock check on my life.

I will let go of what I do not need.

I will take a look at my life and see where I could create space for new items, ideas, people or relationships.

(35)
The Garden

Do you sometimes feel overwhelmed by what is happening around you?

Do you sometimes feel guilty that bad things seem to happen to your friends?

Do you get upset when your friends are going through a rough patch?

All may be fine in your garden (your life), but someone close to you may be experiencing a little upheaval.

You may be called upon for some support.

Try not to get overwhelmed by it all. It is just a shower and it will pass. The sun will shine soon again for all.

This is about a day in the garden when everything appears rosy. The garden in this story is life.

Imagine a garden with beautiful flowers. Each flower needs something different. For each flower there is a season. For each season there is a time. Each flower has its own colours, fragrances and attractiveness. Each flower contributes its own qualities to the garden.

All the flowers do not need water at the same time. Some flowers may need more water than others to survive. Sometimes it is necessary for the flowers that do *not* need much water, to adapt themselves to extra water, because their turn will come when *they* will need more water and the flowers beside them will need less.

And so life in the garden goes on.

The gardener may come out with his hose and seeing a

flower very much in need of water, will turn his hose on fully. The flower beside this one is gazing up at the sun and enjoying the heat and is totally unprepared for a soaking. It gets a bit of a shock. Life seemed to be so good, but all of a sudden this cold shower falls on an otherwise perfect day.

The bees and insects scatter to protect themselves. The other flowers that are not so far away also get a few drops but not to the extent the nearest one does. The flower getting the most of the overspill, gets a bit annoyed. Why should his day be upset, just because he chose to grow beside this fellow who seems to be having problems.

Life is like a garden.

We grow and blossom together. Each taking turns according to our seasons, our wants and our needs. Sometimes just like in the garden, one particular flower (friend) is going through a difficult phase, but there is no need for you to feel guilty, because this time it is *their* turn, and next time it could be yours. Everyone gets his or her turn in the seasons of life.

One day this person (this flower) that is very close to you experiences a time of difficulty. They feel that their wants and needs are not being met. You can offer them your support until they have dealt with their problem. All their tears and trauma may overwhelm you. You may feel that you are being drowned by all the tears, but remember, the tears are just like an overflow for the pain and the anguish they cannot cope with. They are also like the flower that got too much water. They have too much hurt and trauma to deal with at this moment. They just ask that your strong petals can sustain this overflow, until the torrent has settled down.

The next time it may be your turn in the garden of life and they will be your support, until your petals are strong enough to raise their heads to the sunshine once again.

Today you may meet someone in the garden of life that is overwhelmed by all that is happening for them in life. Without taking their issues on board, maybe you can support them until the shower has passed. Today if it is you who is feeling overwhelmed, reach out to a friend, to your angels, your guides, your God. They will stretch out their arms and their wings to support you until the shower has passed.

We all take turns in the garden of life.

(36)
A Hasty Decision

If you are presented with a nice meal and you like it apart from one ingredient, what would you do?

Would you throw the full meal in the dustbin because of the part you do not like, or that you do not find agreeable? Or, would you put that piece to one side, enjoy the rest of the meal, and suggest to the person presenting you with the meal, not to include this particular item of food when preparing a meal for you in the future.

If you are in a relationship and you do not like one particular aspect of the other person's behaviour, do you discard this person and end the relationship, or do you enjoy what you *do* have in common with this person, talk it through, and together try to resolve the aspects of this person's behaviour, which you do not find acceptable.

...Solomon.

(37)
A Void In Your Life

Do you ever feel you look beautiful on the outside, but you are crumbling apart on the inside?

Imagine your body is like a house.

A house, in order to resist the forces of nature, needs to be built on good solid ground. Did *you* have a good solid grounding from the time of your birth?

A house needs a good solid foundation to withstand the rigours of life. Did *you* have a good solid foundation (a solid belief system) to start you off in life?

A house needs good solid walls for support. Uneven or weak walls will crack and eventually fall, bringing with it the roof and all that is attached to it. Did *you* have a good solid support system within your family, especially in the early years?

What happens when you discover your walls are a bit shaky? What happens when you discover cracks in the walls? Do you cover up the cracks with nice wallpaper, every time a crack appears? When this does not work, do you close down that particular room altogether? Do you shut down your feelings? Do you compensate by having a hectic social lifestyle? Do you close down the rooms of your house one after the other, because you have been conditioned to believe they are not suitable for you, and because it only hurts to continue living in them?

Do you close off your feelings and emotions and fail to acknowledge them so as to avoid the pain? Or, do you live in denial of your hurts and pain? Do you treat yourself to material goods that make you feel better for short periods of time i.e. that new outfit, new car, or a new gadget or ornament for your house?

You can survive on a few rooms being in use. (You can survive with limited feelings or emotions). You can even survive by moving down into the cellar. (You may hide your feelings completely). You may hide the reality of what is happening with distractions like alcohol, drugs etc. The only problem here is that the rooms that are not in use are likely to get damp and eventually fall into decay. You can bring new furniture into your house, but the old cracks and damp spots will continue raising their ugly heads. You can hide in the cold dark cellar indefinitely, convincing yourself that this is the life you want. But is it?

You need to ask yourself what can you do before your house falls down around you.

First you may need to clear out and dump, any outdated useless furniture you may have collected over the years. Get rid of old outdated belief systems. Be prepared to let go and change any dysfunctional behaviour and thought patterns, which may no longer be of benefit to you. Conditioning may have been a factor in preventing you from making these changes up until now.

You can take up the old carpets that are covering the dampness in the foundations. You can strip off the old wallpaper that is covering the cracks. But first of all you need to acknowledge that there is a problem. This problem may have been developing over many years. It may have rotted the skirting boards, the floors and the roof.

The most difficult part is opening up those old rooms (opening up to your feelings again). This may be like opening up old wounds. It may be painful initially. However, you do not have to open up all the rooms at the same time. It may have taken many years to close off all those rooms, but it will not take many years to open them up again, providing you get help. You can open up those rooms one at a time. Little by little you can strip off all the old wallpaper and paint.

When you clear out your house it can feel bare and empty for a while. When you let go and discard old patterns of behaviour and conditioning you can feel lonely. The tendency here can be to rush out and bring back some or all of the old furniture (old behaviours, dysfunctional relationships) to fill the empty spaces. You may feel like returning to your old ways because you are lonely. You may find yourself participating in social events with people that you have no wish to relate to, or socialise with. You may feel like rushing out and purchasing old or useless goods, or items for your house (yourself) to fill the void.

When you realise and feel it is safe to do so, you can avail of all the help and support available to you. You can come out of that cold dark cellar into the sunshine.

You can create a new reality with this house by seeing it as it really is, with its great warmth and strength of character. You can create a new reality, but first you must learn to know and accept *you* the core being, as you really are.

This is a time to stand still and look at this great house, this great being that you are, with all your blemishes. Look more closely at the walls of your house and you will see more clearly where, when and how, the damage was done. Look at your foundations and see where they need to be re-enforced.

When you have cleaned out your house, opened the doors and windows, and allowed in fresh air and sunshine, you will have created space in your life for new ideas, fun, joy and laughter.

Light a candle for yourself.

See yourself as you really are.

You are still the perfect being that God created.

You may have picked up blemishes on your journey,

but beneath it all you are perfect.

You have within your possession everything you need

for your journey.

Let the sun shine through your windows (your eyes).

Let the angels support your walls (your arms and legs).

Let God create a new foundation for you from his cloak of eternal life.

(38)
Accepting You

Can you accept what is, or do you immediately try to change "what is," to "what you think" it should be, so you can like and accept it more?

Are you an accepting type of person?

If you are the world is blessed by your presence.

If you are not it may be a time for change, a time for you to change.

You cannot change anyone but yourself.

Can you love what you see, not what you want to see?

You as energy do not change. You grow and evolve. You will always be who you are. You evolve by your own personal learnings. You do not evolve when you continually attempt to change yourself, so that you are acceptable to others.

When you see a beautiful plant, love and enjoy it as it is. Do not try to imagine how it would look *if* it were more beautiful. You have now rejected *what it is now in this moment*. How can it evolve if it is not accepted as it is first? It is not up to you to decide how it could be more beautiful. This is the plant's journey. It is growing and evolving at its own pace. This is not *your* journey. Do not try to travel its journey for it.

You have a beautiful house (your body), but you may not feel comfortable within it. You have a beautiful garden (your surroundings, your family and friends). Sometimes like the garden or the house, you cannot appreciate the beauty that is within you and in that which surrounds you. When you look at yourself, do you wish you were thinner, fatter, taller or more attractive looking? By doing this you are not accepting yourself, as you are first. You cannot leave where you are not at.

Imagine your body as a beautiful house and your surroundings (your family, friends etc.) as a beautiful garden. Do you look around the house at times and think, "If only I could change one thing or another, then it would be a better place to live in?" Do you sometimes look out your window at the garden and feel, that if you could only change or remove certain flowers, that it would then be a nicer place to spend your time?

Sometimes when you look at the garden, you may wish the winter was over and the flowers would shoot out. Your family and friends may be in the winter of life, they may be resting and preparing for spring, they may not come up to your expectations at this moment in time. Do you wish your family were more intelligent, better educated, maturing much faster, were more acceptable to you, and would get better jobs, better homes etc?

Do you wish you were more acceptable to you? Maybe you too are going through the seasons of life, going through a rough patch healing from old traumas, hurts and wounds. Like the plant, the garden, the self, the family, they all need to be accepted wherever they are at. This is *your* journey and it is also *their* journey. If you invest too much of yourself, your beliefs, your time, into trying to change what is around you and any of those investments disappear, part of you also disappears.

The acceptance of yourself and of others is like the beginning of writing a book. Only when the pen has touched the paper, has the book begun. From there you can move on, but first the pen must touch the paper. You must accept yourself first. If you cannot accept yourself, how can you begin to accept someone else? You need to see yourself as you truly are. If the value you place on yourself is based on what others have achieved and how they see you, that is not true self-acceptance. Can you allow others to see you as you truly are? Can you accept friends calling and seeing your house in total chaos (you in total chaos)? Can you accept others seeing your pain, your sorrow, and your hurt? Can you do likewise with your family and friends? Accepting what is – that is total acceptance.

Your instinctive reaction may be to cover it all up, clean up the house (the self), wipe away the tears and make everything *appear* to look good. This is not self-acceptance; because what is really happening is that you are hiding the pain and hurt.

When was the last time you looked and accepted yourself for who you are, and not how others accept or see you? Everything that has ever happened to you up to this moment, has created the person you are today. Everything that happens for you today, will create the person that you will be tomorrow.

Today you are beautiful. It is where you are today that is important – not where you are going tomorrow.

Accept what is.

The child of the sweep is still a child – *that is what is.*

The child of the king is still a child – *that is what is.*

If you were lying in bed with a broken leg – *that is what is.*

There is only what you can do or cannot do at this moment in time.

When you accept "what is," you can then move forward to create what you would prefer next. You always have choices in what you create, but you must first accept "what is" right now.

Affirmation:

Today I ask you God, guides, angels, higher power

to take my hands, help me to listen to the silence.

Help me listen to my heart, listen to my breath and

listen to myself.

Help me accept that which surrounds me.

Help me accept everything as it is and everyone as they are.

Help me accept the sound of the birds, the growth of nature, the seasons and most of all help me to accept myself.

(39)
I Am Me

In all the world, there is no one exactly like me. There are persons who have some part of me, but no one adds up exactly like me. Therefore, everything that comes out of me is authentically mine because I alone chose it.

I own everything about me. – My body, including everything it does.

My mind, including all its thoughts and ideas.

My eyes, including the images of all they behold.

My feelings, whatever they may be – anger, joy, frustration, love, disappointment, excitement.

My mouth, and all the words that come out of it, polite, sweet or rough, correct or in-correct.

My voice, loud or soft, and all my actions, whether they be to others or to myself.

I own my fantasies, my dreams, my hopes, and my fears.

I own all my triumphs and successes, all my failures and mistakes.

Because I own all of me, I can become intimately acquainted with me. By so doing I can love me, and be friendly with me in all my parts. I can then make it possible for all of me to work in my best interests.

I know there are aspects about myself that puzzle me, and other aspects that I do not know. But as long as I am friendly and loving to myself, I can courageously and hopefully look for the solutions to the puzzles and for ways to find out more about me.

However I look or sound, whatever I say or do, and

whatever I think and feel at any given moment in time is me. This is authentic and represents where I am at that moment in time.

When I review later how I looked and sounded, what I said and did, and how I thought and felt, some parts may turn out to be unfitting. I can discard that which is unfitting, and keep that which proved fitting, and invent something new for that which I discarded.

I can see, hear, feel, think, say, and do. I have the tools to survive, to be close to others, to be productive, and to make sense and order out of the world of people and things outside of me.

I own me, and therefore I can engineer me.

I am me and I am okay.

(40)
The Bird In The Cage

The bird could be you. The cage is life.

Do you feel you are, or have been in captivity?

Do you feel restricted to the point of suffocation?

This story could be about you. It could be about so many people you know. This is a story to bring awareness to you of how lack of freedom can affect you or another.

This is the scene from a story told about a woman who is now fifty years of age. The story of this woman's life, is likened to that of a tiny bird born into captivity.

In the beginning it is just a tiny little bird fluttering around in a lovely spacious cage. (The cage is life). The bird is quite healthy. It is being fed and its cage is cleaned out regularly, but with conditions. It is often told what to do. But more often it is told what not to do. "Don't be angry." "Take what you get." "Don't be sad." "Don't show fear." "Don't be assertive." "Don't ask questions." "Don't ask why." "What will the neighbours think?" – This is the beginning of the conditioning.

The bird grows bigger but the cage does not. The conditioning does not change. The bird starts to feel more uncomfortable as the years pass. Its legs are cramped and its wings are under developed.

How many of us have experienced these feelings? Never being allowed to stretch. Never being allowed to grow. How many of us do not know any other way of being? Difficult relationships, difficult family situations difficult work situations, difficult living conditions?

This bird has believed and has been conditioned to

believe there is no other way. The pains and the aches get worse (constant headaches, colds and flu's). The bird says, "I know this is not a healthy place for me to be, but if I get out of here I could die. I will not know how to survive on my own. I am fearful of change. If I stay here, I will die from lack of nourishment, lack of exercise, lack of love, lack of life."

The bird feels helpless and hopeless about her situation. She prays night and day for freedom.

Then one day a guide in the form of a friend comes along and sees the conditions under which this bird is living. She gently opens the cage door. The bird sees the possibilities out there – blue skies, fresh air and freedom. (A brighter future, functional relationships, freedom of choice). Although she sees the great possibilities out there, she nonetheless feels fearful and apprehensive.

Conditioning has taught her to be fearful of change.

It has taught her:

"Don't rock the boat."

"Take what you get."

"Aren't you lucky to be alive."

The bird has realised she is only existing not living. She knows she must now learn to trust if she is to survive. In order to live life to the full, she must first trust enough to leave the cage. Trust in her guides, trust in herself and trust in God.

She does learn to trust a little, although with great apprehension and fear. The guide supports her while she gently eases out one wing, then one leg. Little by little the bird emerges slowly and painfully. As she leaves the cage she begins to see and believe what is possible with freedom. With freedom, comes the possibility of flight, of soaring to new heights, travelling to new lands, and seeking new learnings.

Only time, guidance and gentle healing will soothe the

scars that life up until now has imposed on her. This will not happen in a day or a week but in time this bird will soar to her true heights and recognise her true spirit.

- You too can believe in new possibilities.
- You too can leave your cage.
- You too can spread your wings.
- You too can soar to new heights.
- You too can learn to love and be loved.
- You too can be free to live again.
- Help can be just a door away.

Affirmation:

I choose to be free.

I seek freedom.

I am free.

I spread my wings and soar to new heights.

(41)

Life In The Fast Lane

Do you feel you are moving too fast?

Do you feel that your life is out of control?

Are you feeling you have lost control of your life?

Imagine your life is likened to a racehorse. Ask yourself, "Am I in control of this powerful gift?"

Was there a time in your life when you had the reins in your hands and you felt you had everything under control, then one day you woke up and found that everything and everyone was moving so much faster than you? You may have thought you had a tight grip on the reins of life, but all of a sudden everything around you seemed to be out of control. When this happened you might have felt like you were sitting on a cart, hitched to a racehorse that was going so fast, that you felt you could not control him, or slow him down.

How are you now?

- Do you find that the tighter you hold on to the reins the more tired you become? The more tired you become, the less you are in control of the horse (your life)?
- Do you feel you have lost control of the reins?
- Is your life moving so fast that you are having difficulty coping with it? You may be hoping that this horse (life) might slow down of its own accord so you can regain control of the reins (regain control of your life).
- Do you feel this horse is pulling you along at such speed, that you have no choice over which direction you are going?

- Do you feel that you have lost control of your own destiny?

You may decide to ask for help. Ask your friends, family, guides, God or your angels. The problem is that since the first time you noticed you were travelling too fast, you may have picked up pace, and now feel you are travelling at breakneck speed.

Your God, guides or your angels now have very few choices.

1. They could step across in front of you on your path and stop you suddenly in your tracks. This could come in the form of a minor or major accident. The problem is that a sudden stop at the speed you are travelling, could mean you could get seriously injured or even killed.

2. They could slow you down gradually over a period of time. This could come in the form of constant sickness, or ailments severe enough, to slow you down or grind you to a halt.

What can you do if you feel the pace you are travelling at, is almost completely out of your control?

- First, grab a tight hold of the reins. Find out what you can do for yourself to slow you down.
- Seek help to slow yourself down if necessary.
- However difficult, try not to let go of the reins altogether, otherwise the horse (life) will take you wherever *he* feels like taking you.
- Try not to hand over the reins to someone else to slow down the horse. (Try not to hand over all responsibility for your health and your life to someone else).
- When you come to a halt, try and find out what caused you to speed up in the first place.

Ask yourself some questions:

1. What kept you at this pace until now?
2. Could it all have started before you were born i.e. induced birth, traumatic delivery, last minute arrangements, or born prematurely as a result of an accident or trauma?
3. Did you experience impatience from those around you in your early years of development? Were your parents, childminders, or other family members impatient with the pace you eat, or learned to feed yourself? Or, with the length of time it took for you to be toilet trained? Or, with the pace you learned to walk and talk?
4. Were there expectations from you as a child, to equal or sometimes surpass the accomplishments of fellow siblings and friends?
5. Did you feel rushed and pressurised into trying to keep pace with everybody around you at school, at home, or in your place of work?
6. Did you feel you were falling behind, or that everybody else seemed further ahead?
7. Were you trying to get it all over and done with quickly?
8. Were you running away from something or somebody i.e. an abusive or dysfunctional relationship or family situation?
9. Was there a crisis or trauma, which you did not feel able or ready to deal with?
10. Were you driven by anxiety, or fear, or of the possible consequences of what would happen, if you slowed down or stopped?
11. Had you lost the ability to go with your gut feelings and live in the moment?

12. Was it conditioning that was driving you at such a fast pace?
13. Did you believe everything would be better somewhere ahead?

As an adult it may now be the time for you to take back full control of the reins. Take back your own power. Get help if necessary to slow yourself down. This will enable you to travel at the pace that is safer and more comfortable for you on your journey.

Affirmation:

I will live my life at my own pace.

I will not allow others or their expectations to push me beyond my capabilities.

I will learn how to relax and slow down.

I will regain control of my life and my health.

With each breath I take, I will slow myself down.

I will seek help and support from those who have mastered the ability to relax and slow down.

Chore for the week read: "SLOW ME DOWN GOD."

***Slow Me Down God**

Slow me down God; ease the pounding of my heart by the quieting of my mind. Steady my hurried pace with the vision of the eternal reach of time.

Give me, amidst the confusion of my day, the calmness of the everlasting hills. Break the tensions of my nerves and muscles with the soothing music of the singing streams that live in my memory.

Help me to know the magical, restoring power of sleep. Teach me the art of taking one-minute vacations… of slowing down to look at a flower, to chat with a friend, to pat a dog, to read a few lines from a good book, to go for a nice leisurely walk, to dream.

Remind me each day of the fable of the hare and the tortoise that I may know that the race is not always to the swift; that there is more in life than increasing speed.

Let me look upward into the branches of the towering oak and know that it grew great and strong because it grew slowly and well.

Slow me down God, and inspire me to send my roots deep into the soil of life's enduring values that I may grow upward toward the stars of my greater destiny.

**Author unknown.*

(42)
The Great Oak And The Small Oak

The great oak is the adult, and the small oak is the child.

This is the story of the great oak which is you, with all your learnings and abilities. The small oak is the child, who is endeavouring to learn from you, his environment and all those around him. He has no sense of boundaries or limitations yet.

If the great oak "*you*" moves every time the small oak calls, the great oak loses the ability to hold on to the soil and the solid ground or to remain rooted. The small oak is still growing so can set down its roots anywhere at any time. If the great oak continually uproots and moves itself it will have great difficulty holding on to the earth when the storms arrive. The great oak having no firm roots, will fall leaving the small oak with no protection from the strong winds and the harsh elements.

You are the great oak. Those of a young age depend on you for guidance and protection and need your solidity. If every time they call, you come running, you will uproot yourself from what you are doing, and at a later time you will have to set yourself down and try to continue where you left off.

The small oak (the child) is depending on you for their learnings. If they learn from you that you can be moved from what you are doing or where you are at, at a moments notice – they in turn will not learn how to be grounded and stay put until it is convenient for them to move. This amount of constant moving for you, can cause exhaustion.

Do you react instantly when your children or someone else calls you, stopping what you are doing, to facilitate their every wish or command? Or, do you say, "When I am ready I will help you deal with the problem?" Or, "When I am ready I will help you sort out your difficulty?" Did you ever hear a parent or child minder say, "I can never get anything finished when the children are around?" Why not? Did you ever ask yourself, is it because you react and move on demand? You are not learning and neither are they. Do you wonder what sort of an example you are setting for your little oak? If you stop what you are doing every time they call, what sort of message are you projecting to your little child?

Are you projecting a message saying?

"What I am doing does not matter."

"What I am saying does not matter."

"My time does not matter."

"I do not matter."

This little oak (the child) observes your every move, because it is part of you. It chose you and came here to learn from you, to observe your weaknesses and your strengths. Your little oak will mirror back to you all your behaviours.

- How does your little oak see you? (How does your child see you)?
- Are your roots connected firmly to the ground? (Do you stand your ground)?
- Are you well grounded in your decisions and beliefs and not given to childish reactions and behaviours in an adult situation?
- Are you a strong great oak, not easily swayed by the wind, or does all that is happening around you easily sway you?
- Do you resist the urge to respond instantly to the wishes and demands of the little oak? (Do you resist the whims of your child)?

- Do you have strong branches to support the little oak in times of trouble? (Do you maintain your own physical, emotional and mental health, so you can support your child in times of need)?
- Do you have plenty of healthy leaves on your branches to shield the small oak from the storms, cold, wind and rain, until he grows his own leaves? (Have you availed of all the information and learnings necessary to guard and protect you and your child from life's illnesses and traumas)? If you have done this, then the support will be there for both of you.

As the little oak (child) grows older and stronger, it will develop its own strong branches and leaves (its patterns, strengths and belief systems). As this little oak (child) develops, do you encourage them to be grounded and to feel secure in whatever they choose to do, or in the decisions they make in life? As they grow older, do you teach them that whatever decisions they make, – they themselves are responsible for those decisions? Or, do you allow a behaviour pattern that started in childhood, to continue into adulthood, e.g. where every time they got into any sort of difficulty, they called you, and you came running?

How are you behaving now?

For example now they are older and have their own means of transport, are they regularly allowing it to run out of petrol? Do you go and rescue them whenever they are stranded, regardless of the time, whether it be day or night, regardless of how you are feeling yourself or how you may be otherwise engaged at the time?

When they forget to bring their own door key, do you jump out of bed every other night to let them in? When they forget to collect their laundry, do you go out of your way to collect it for them despite all the chores you have to do for yourself? When they call you at 4.a.m. in the morning to say they have missed their lift home once again, do you jump out of bed and go and collect them, without even thinking of the consequences for yourself, and the lack of learning for them?

Is all of this still happening on a regular basis?

After years of this behaviour, this great oak becomes worn out and exhausted. It no longer produces nice green leaves. There is very little growth in this tree, because it allowed itself to be up-rooted so many times. Its branches are now twisted and broken (from so many people swinging from them).

From a great oak that children once played near, a great oak that offered support and protection for many small oaks, here now stands a bare and lonely tree. This tree that was once a great oak has lost its identity. Its branches are no longer strong and firm. They have lost their leaves. It has no protection now from the wind or rain. Its roots are exposed to the elements, to the cold and the frost. Because the great oak moved so many times its roots did not get enough time to grow deep into the soil, where they would be protected. This great oak that protected and shielded so many, has no protection itself now in its old age. It has very little energy now. It is losing the will to live.

The small oak (child) mirroring the poor role modelling of the great oak (parent) has moved on. It is constantly on the move never staying anywhere for any length of time and answering to everyone's beck and call.

Fellow great oaks (friends seeing the behaviour of the great oak) have also moved away to be in more secure ground (secure living and family conditions) for their later years. They have also moved to be near fellow great oaks, (likeminded people) for support when the storms arrive. This may not look like a happy ending for this great oak. But where there is life there is still hope. This great oak may not have had a good role model to teach it, and to learn from, when it was young itself.

If you are still a young oak, maybe you can learn something from this story. If you are an older great oak, you can stop the behaviour that is ageing and exhausting you. You may need to learn to take care of yourself, where you are at, in this present moment in time. If you continue to move, it could be detrimental to the possibility of any further growth, or any possible healing from the past. You may need to encourage your roots to take hold no matter how little. If you do not do so at this stage, you could topple and die with the next big wind that blows. (That next big illness).

The first thing you must do in order to survive is to stop moving. Stop allowing others to move and sway you. Stand still. Trim off any damaged roots or branches that are weighing you down (get rid of anything in your life that is weighing you down). The more you trim the rotten and decayed branches (get rid of outdated belief systems and dysfunctional behaviours), the more sunshine and water the tree will receive, to nurture its core through the good branches. Put good healthy compost around the roots that are exposed. (Bring good and positive things into your life i.e. new ideas, good nourishing and healthy food, kind and supportive friends, healthy and happy relationships, happy and joyous moments).

The roots may not fully recover from all the moving, but the longer they stay in the one position, the better chance the tree has of surviving to a ripe old age.

Affirmation:

I will stop moving unnecessarily.

I will stop and think before moving when someone calls.

I will not be swayed by anyone.

I will be still.

I will survive the storm.

(43)
The Only Reality We Know

Is there someone you know who may be creating the only reality they know?

Are you creating the only reality you know, "your reality" meaning what is real and normal for you?

This can be your way of living, your way of life, your way of dealing with everyone and everything around you, your way of coping, your way of surviving in life, your belief system.

If you believe that *your* particular way of being, *your* way of behaviour, *your* way of coping and dealing with life is normal then that is *your* reality. This could mean that you see dysfunctional, addictive, controlling or aggressive behaviour as normal. Some of these behaviours could be harmful to you or to others i.e. family or friends. If it is the only way *you* have learned how to deal and cope with life, then it is the only reality *you* know or may have known all your life.

However this does not mean that your behaviour is acceptable or appropriate behaviour.

Some of these behaviours you will have learned from the role models you had as a child such as parents, teachers, or family members. You will also have discovered some of these behaviours as coping methods yourself. You may not have experienced happy, functional and harmonious relationships. You may have observed many unhappy and dysfunctional relationships over many years. Within these relationships there may have been constant arguments with abusive, addictive or aggressive behaviour. If this has been your reality to date, it may have seemed like a normal reality to you in forming a belief system of how life is.

A change in this belief system (this reality) could be

brought about by a change in your attitude, a new awareness, a new belief system, a new relationship, a new job or a change in living conditions.

With a new awareness you may enter a happy, harmonious and functional relationship, or the relationship you are already in, could change and become more harmonious and happy. You may adapt and feel comfortable with this relationship for a time. As time passes you may find yourself sabotaging the relationship, because this type of relationship is unfamiliar to you. You may sabotage this relationship without being consciously aware of it, e.g. by constantly picking arguments, by being impatient or intolerant over minor issues. You may also sabotage this relationship by inappropriate behaviour patterns. When you do this and disharmony and unhappiness sets in, you will find you are now back on familiar ground again.

You have now created once again the only reality you know, when it comes to relationships i.e. disharmony and unhappiness.

If rejection is your reality:

You could have first experienced this rejection prior to birth, during childhood or adulthood. If a child feels rejection by a parent or parents, it is most likely the child will in turn reject itself. The only reality you may now know is *rejection*.

If you find you are being accepted, appreciated or admired by someone who loves or cares about you, you may behave in such a way that will create a situation, which will bring about rejection. You may also find if you are praised or rewarded for work you have done, you may create a situation that will bring about criticism or rejection.

Ways of causing rejection include minimising what you have achieved or accomplished, aggressive or abusive behaviour, overeating, under eating, self-rejection, self-harming or unhygienic behaviour patterns. As long as you can bring about a situation where you create and experience rejection, the level of this rejection is often irrelevant.

If chaos is your reality:

You may have experienced chaos in your family as a child. You may have lived in a home where there were constant arguments, abusive or aggressive behaviour, you the child never knowing when you would feel safe or secure. Inconsistent boundaries, no set time tables for sleeping or meal times, conflicting and confusing behaviour patterns, and poor role modelling by your parents. All of these can contribute to a reality of chaos.

If abuse is your reality:

You may find yourself in abusive and aggressive situations, sometimes without even being consciously aware of how you got yourself into the given situation. Because abuse may be your reality, you may be attracting aggressive or abusive behaviour (physical, emotional, mental or sexual). This may continue to happen until you find the cause and then get help to heal from it.

For all of us there are many types of "reality." These can be control, unhappiness, disharmony, abuse, rejection, chaos, fear and many others.

Initially it may be difficult to live with anything other than the reality you know. When you become aware of *how* you are recreating *your* reality over and over again, and how much hurt and harm it is doing to you and those around you, it is only then that you can make the necessary changes to learn and heal.

You can have a functional and healthy life if you are prepared to make these changes. You may need help to recognise when, and how, your behaviour is affecting yourself and those around you.

You may need help and guidance to see that the reality you are working with, may have been the only reality you ever knew. You can change all of this to a new, happier, healthier and functional way of living (a new reality).

Case History:

Ann was born the second eldest of fourteen children. She learned at a very early age how to control. For her it was the only safe position to be in. You could not get hurt if you were in control, (or so she believed). Both her parents were very strict, her mother being the dominant one. Ann and other members of the family had difficulty relating to their father. He was a very silent man and the only time he really conversed with his family, was after he had consumed a certain amount of alcohol.

Over the years his drinking binges became more and more frequent. Arguments would develop between both parents over shortages of money. On the occasional Sunday her father would go to morning church, and not return until after closing time in the local pub or well into the next morning. Ann would hear her mother crying and shouting, because of his late arrival home and the burned dinner which she had prepared for him many hours earlier. Her father's drinking and late arrivals became a regular occurrence. Her mother annoyed and frustrated by all this, would regularly pack her bags and leave the house. Sometimes it might only be for an hour, sometimes a day, sometimes it would only be a threat, but it had the same effect on Ann. She lived in fear that one day her mother would actually leave the home and never come back.

Sunday was one of the worst days of the week for Ann. Her father would attend the 11.00a.m. service in the local church with a promise of being home for dinner at 1.pm. With each hour that passed after 1.00p.m. and no sign of her father returning, Ann would become tense and apprehensive. As evening time approached and with still no sign of him coming home, Ann would become crippled with fear, because of the possible consequences of her father arriving home late, drunk, and disorderly.

Over the years as Ann grew older, she tried to compensate for her father's lack of responsibility. Her father was never abusive with alcohol, but his tolerance level to the family's ups and downs became less and less over the years. Ann gave her mother most of the money she earned, and all the time she could spare, feeling in some way this would make amends, for the pain caused to her mother by her father's drinking and general behaviour.

As Ann grew older she learned how she could control and fix situations that seemed impossible and out of control to everyone else. In later years she took up employment where she felt many people needed fixing, – she became a nurse. She also learned to control her feelings. The child, who could not control her father's sickness, was now the adult who was going to fix the world and everyone in it. She was a good nurse and worked way beyond the call of duty. She learned that if you did not "feel" you did not get hurt. "Feelings" were something you read about in a book. They were something other people experienced, but they were not for Ann, a luxury she believed she could not afford.

In later years Ann got married and had two children. Her husband, like her father, also had a drink problem. This time Ann was smarter. Every morning when her husband was leaving for work, she would ask him how much money he had in his pocket. She would say she needed the amount he had and more to pay for something for the house, herself or the children. Her husband's behaviour patterns were similar to that of her father. He would come home when he chose, blame others for his lateness and his drunkenness, and make promises, which were never kept. Ann had, in marrying a man similar to her father, started a new life of "the only reality she knew." The only reality she knew was chaos, never knowing, fear of relaxing, fear of not being in control, fear of rejection.

Ann made it virtually impossible for her husband to overindulge in alcohol, but he still somehow managed to get drunk. If there was a gold medal for control, Ann said she would have got it during those years. She listed off her tactics. She would sometimes go out drinking with her husband, but "forget" to bring enough money for extra drink. Sometimes Ann would pretend to feel ill about an hour before they were due to leave for a night out, so both she and her husband would have to stay at home. At times she would delay the baby-sitter so they would go out late, and arrive at the bar just before closing time. Sometimes she would mislay the keys of the car, to delay them both from going out.

As Ann's control got stronger, her husband's desperation got stronger too. His tactics were, he would go and have a few drinks with the lads after work and arrive home drunk, and with not enough time left for each of them to change their clothes and go out again. Sometimes he would send one of his mates to pick Ann up. He got a few sets of car keys cut, so as to avoid them getting "lost" by Ann.

As the years passed, Ann's health deteriorated. Her whole life had become one of control and constant stress. She would lie awake until the early hours of the morning, waiting for the screeching of tyres announcing her husband's return home. At last Ann could relax now that he had returned home, or could she? She still had to spend another few hours interrogating him, screaming at him, crying with relief one moment that he was home safe, then the next moment crying with anger and frustration that he did not seem to care about how she felt or how she worried.

Their two children were now both very much aware of the problems in their home and could see that "Mom is always crying and Dad is never at home." Ann threatened suicide if her husband did not stop drinking to excess. This was a more serious type of control and worked for a while. But then there were two children to consider, so Ann was unlikely to resort to this extreme measure, or so her husband believed.

Since she never did attempt to commit suicide, this threat wore a little thin as far as Ann's husband was concerned. She tried every tactic in the book now to control him like staying out all night herself, so he could not leave the children. – He got a baby-sitter. She tried to stay drinking as long as he drank, but he won again – she would then have to drive the car home in a drunken state. Her husband never seemed to suffer the after effects of his drinking, but Ann would have to get up early the next morning with a hangover and drive the children to school.

Eventually the financial problems started to escalate. More money was borrowed to enable him to pay his bills. (Not alone was Ann trying to control him, but she was also enabling him at this stage as well). Ann felt it was her responsibility to pay back the borrowed money and found herself under more pressure.

She took on a part-time job to enable her to pay off some of the debts, but since her husband's irresponsible behaviour remained unchanged, matters did not improve. For Ann the more money she earned, the more he spent. The more time she spent out of the home working, the more opportunities he had to stay in the pub. Eventually Ann realised her health could not sustain her husband's behaviour or her own.

She attended for therapy and joined an awareness group. In time she felt able to stand back and observe and recognise the part she was playing in the family's problems. By now however her survival techniques, controlling, denial and enabling, had almost cost her, her home, her children and her health. Her husband saw her detachment as not caring about him. Ann started to take control of her own life, realising she could not take responsibility for anyone but herself, and what is more she could not change or control anyone but herself.

Her husband left her to go into a new relationship with a woman who did not nag him (or so he said), but controls him in a nicer way. After all you can control much better by being nice than being nasty, but it *is* control nonetheless. (How many of us try to control by being silent, by being abusive, by fear, by strength, by kindness)?

After many years of therapy Ann still has to be on her guard and watch her behaviour patterns. Habit is a difficult thing to break. It is the "not knowing" when the rows will begin, that can cause tension in Ann. At least when the chaos and rows are happening she feels she can do something, because she is back on familiar ground again. When she finds herself recreating scenarios from the past Ann has to consciously tell herself to "stop," and then ask herself what is happening for her at this moment in time, she has to ask herself, what is she feeling? Is it fear, is it anxiety, is it hurt, guilt, shame, tension etc?

There are many people whose lives and relationships have been very similar to Ann's. After months of no rows, no quarrels, no arguments, they may start to feel uneasy. Even with a new and healthy relationship, they may still find themselves getting uptight and anxious when old memories are triggered. They may not consciously pick an argument, but they may keep niggling and picking on their partner until a full-blown row develops.

They may not understand their behaviour at the time, but during therapy sessions when they describe their actions and reflect back, only then may they get an insight into their behaviour and the reason for it. With help from a therapist, they can begin to fully understand, how they were in fact trying to bring about a situation again, which they had been so familiar with, this being the only reality they knew.

When you become aware of the reality *you* may be recreating over and over again, then and only then, can you with help and guidance make the necessary changes to heal your life.

(44)
How Can They Learn?

Do you allow others to learn?

Do you allow your children to learn?

Do you allow yourself to learn?

Baby:

Observe a baby who is learning to walk, it stands up, takes a step and falls down. It does not hurt itself, because it does not go too far. The next thing the baby will do is climb up beside a chair and walk around it. After that, it will attempt to walk from one chair to the next one and so on.

One day the baby will attempt to make a longer journey, a longer distance between chairs. We can see the baby will not make the journey, but the baby is going to try anyway. He makes it about halfway across the room and topples over. What do we do? We run and grab him before he falls. Now baby does not know how far he went, or how far he can go. His last attempt was interrupted half way, so for him that journey was nonexistent.

When his mother is not looking, off he goes walking again, not knowing how to judge the distance. He does make it a little further, but bangs his head on the corner of the table bruising his forehead and causing quite a swelling. His mother gets into a panic, and after cleaning him up; she confines him to the playpen for the afternoon. This has now curtailed his learning.

Mary:

What about little Mary who had limited abilities where maths were concerned? Mary's father completed her homework for her whenever he could. Mary struggled through school and year after year she failed her maths exams, because her Dad was obviously not there to assist her on the day of the exams.

Mary never came to terms with her limited maths abilities. She could have taken up employment where her other abilities would have been recognised and encouraged, but her father insisted on her staying in school and studying for an academic career. Mary did not know what she was capable of. Every time she tried to accomplish something herself her father stepped in and completed it for her. He thought he was helping her, but in fact he was preventing her from learning about her own capabilities. Mary's level of incompetence did not become apparent, until her father used his influence to get her that top job in the accounts department. Her father could not do her work for her so she lost her job.

Johnny:

How many times do we hear parents say, "Johnny does not even know how to wash a cup?" What happened to him when he broke his first cup? We grabbed hold of him, gave him a good talking to and would not allow him to wash the dishes again. What happened the day young Johnny tried to wire a plug on the electric kettle? He caused an electrical short, which knocked off the electricity in the entire house. Because of the shock and the reaction from his family, as an adult, Johnny will not attempt to repair anything electrical again, even down to something simple and necessary.

Jenny:

What about the day Jenny made her first dinner? She burned the dinner and her hand. She was never allowed to even try cooking again. Now that she is married, she attends cooking classes in order to learn how to prepare a basic meal.

At times we do not allow our children to learn. We try to save them from hurt and pain, but like the baby, sometimes the learning experience of a minor hurt at an early age, can prevent a major hurt in later life.

Now ask yourself if you can relate to any of these stories.

Do you allow your children to learn and explore?

Do you allow others to learn?

Do you feel you are a better person by doing for others rather than encouraging them to do for themselves?

Do you want to change?

You can change your own behaviour.

Ask for help to be patient with yourself and your learnings.

Be patient with others and their learnings.

Allow others their mistakes. By their mistakes they learn.

We cannot take anyone where we ourselves have not been.

Affirmation:

I will allow my children to learn.

I will allow others to learn.

I will allow myself to learn.

(45)
A Boulder On Your Path

A boulder on your path is symbolic of a problem you may encounter on your journey through life.

Do you feel your journey through life is, or has been blocked by unexplained happenings?

Do you feel there are times when you have difficulty moving on with your life?

Do you sometimes feel, that there are insurmountable obstacles on your path?

Do you feel no matter how hard you try to succeed on your journey, there is someone or something blocking, stopping or delaying you?

Sometimes on your journey, you may come across a boulder or obstacle on your path. This could happen during childhood or it could happen at any stage of your life.

Your guides, God, your angels could have placed this boulder there in an attempt to slow you down or create a diversion on your journey. This boulder could be to facilitate a learning, or indeed stop you on your journey. It could take the form of an accident, ill health, family, social or work related problems.

You may see this boulder as insurmountable, or as an end to your journey, especially if it is very large and appears suddenly and without warning. Nobody goes through life without experiencing some obstacles (boulders) on their path.

Imagine it is a great obstacle that has appeared on your path. It comes as quite a shock to you, especially if it is the first time anything like this has ever happened to you. You may not have sufficient tools (enough resources or learnings) to deal with it.

You see this major boulder on the road. It is too large to go around it. You cannot get through it (you do not have the tools to process it). You cannot move it (you have not got the strength). You may go into hopelessness because you cannot see your way around it.

You may exhaust yourself chipping away at this major obstacle (trauma) on your own. You may believe that you must shift the entire boulder before you can move on. You may need to look at the alternatives you have. If you can create enough space to get past this boulder by using the tools you *do* have, (the experiences and learnings you already have in life), you can return at a later date with help i.e. counsellors, therapists etc., to deal with and process this major obstacle (trauma).

This boulder may have traumatised, delayed and shocked you, but it has not killed you. You have survived your ordeal.

Sometimes it can take years, to obtain all of the learnings that you need, in order to deal with the obstacles you encounter on your path. However, it is knowing you can actually move on and get help to deal with them that is important. Denying the boulder is there will not resolve the problem. It is not going to go away of its own accord. You will eventually need to deal with it – that is part of your learning here.

If you bypass your boulder and do not deal with it, acquire your learnings (tools for life), as soon as you can and then another boulder falls on your path, you are now caught between two boulders. Now that you are trapped on your journey, you cannot go on, and you cannot go back. You did not learn from the first boulder at all. You did not acquire the tools in life that would help you move along your path, or you did not avail or hold on to the tools that were necessary to help you on your journey.

But supposing you *have* learned. Supposing you *have* the tools that got you through the first boulder (the first obstacle in your life), those tools will play a major part in getting you through the many other obstacles, you may encounter on your future journey.

See the tools you have now.

Take time out to look at those tools (the learnings you have achieved). Do not deny your problems (obstacles, boulders). Use the tools that are available to you to process them to the best of your abilities as they happen. Eventually with help you may be able to clear away all the obstacles on your path. (Deal with all your issues and heal from them).

Sit down, take a deep breath and ask yourself:

- Have you passed a boulder way back on your path?
- What learnings (tools) do you have now for dealing with this obstacle?
- How big was this boulder (this obstacle)?
- Has another boulder now appeared on your path?
- Do you have the tools to deal with it?
- Do you know where to start looking for the tools you had when dealing with the previous boulder?

Try to find the tools that can help you, from within yourself.

You may also need professional help.

Ask your guides, your God, your angels for help.

Ask for help in directing you to the source of help best suited to your needs.

Help is available for you – all you need to do is ask.

Life:

For a long time it had seemed to me that life was about to begin – real life.

But there was always some obstacle in the way, something to be got through first. Some unfinished business, time still to serve, a debt to be paid, then life would begin.

At last it dawned on me that these obstacles are my life.

* *Author unknown.*

(46)
The Flowerbed

The Flowerbed is life.

Are you constantly on the move?

Do you move from place to place, job to job, relationship to relationship, never really stopping or staying in one place for any length of time?

Do you have difficulty setting down roots?

Maybe it is time for you to stop and ask yourself what is happening for you.

Imagine a giant flowerbed.

This is symbolic of life.

Two people meet each other and decide they will start a new life together. We will see the two people as two trees. We will see the flowerbed as the space they have provided for themselves.

The two trees grow side by side in peace and harmony in this flowerbed. As time passes the two trees produce some little trees. The flowerbed is still the same size. The two original trees (people) continue to grow, sometimes towards each other, other times apart.

The little trees (children) are also growing at different paces, each having their own individual needs and requirements.

The size of the flowerbed (home) does not change, but the little trees (children) grow quite fast. The stronger ones overshadowing the weaker ones, the taller ones cutting out the light from the smaller ones. With the larger ones taking up the most space, the smaller ones may feel they are not getting enough nourishment.

Imagine there are now five trees (five people) in this flowerbed (this home). One of the trees (children) decides that the space for him is not large enough for his growth and development. He feels he is being suffocated by his fellow trees, so he decides to move out to a much larger flowerbed with other trees (other people), where he will have sufficient room to grow and develop. As time passes by, he begins to feel restricted and overshadowed in this new flowerbed, so he moves on again.

This pattern continues for years. Every time he sets down his roots he feels he has to pull them up and move on again. This tree (person) is not growing because he never stays anywhere long enough to receive nourishment from the earth, which supports life.

While he was away, his family (fellow trees) had expanded themselves and taken up most of the space and nourishment in the flowerbed. One day he decides to return to his original flowerbed (home). At first his fellow trees (brother, sister and parents) are excited to see him so they shuffle around and tighten up and adjust themselves to make room for him. They believe he is only returning for a short stay and this is only a temporary inconvenience.

It is not long before this visiting tree (person) feels uncomfortable and crowded out again. He now decides to take himself on two weeks holiday to give his fellow trees a break and a bit of space. As soon as he leaves his fellow trees (family members) stretch out their roots once again and settle back into their original places.

After the two weeks holidays are over this tree (person) returns home once again, but this time his fellow trees are less than friendly. They are not prepared to disturb themselves or make any effort to allow him to fit in.

This coming and going goes on with this tree (person) for many years. He never stays anywhere long enough to get nourishment from the soil, or nurturing from life. He does not allow his roots time to become connected to the earth, or to allow himself to develop and grow. He does not stay anywhere long enough to meet like-minded fellow trees (people). As a result of all this moving his roots have remained short and shallow, so when the storm comes he is likely to be toppled over. (He is likely to topple and possibly fall with the first major trauma that life deals him).

If he felt uncomfortable and unhappy with his fellow trees (family members) in the first flowerbed (his home), what is it that keeps bringing him back home again and again? Does he have a problem dealing with difficult situations outside his home and learning from them? Does he have a belief system, that people should adjust and compromise for him whenever he decides they should? Does he have difficulty creating a new reality for himself? Does he have difficulty creating a safe and secure space for himself?

This little tree has lost his belief in himself and his sense of self because of his constant moving. He has become ungrounded, insecure, scared and unsettled. Where can he go and what can he do now?

Could this story be about you?

Maybe it is time to stand still, it is easy to topple a moving object.

Ask yourself what is it you want out of life:

- Do you want a flowerbed (home) for yourself to grow and develop and to set down your roots?
- Do you want a place where other like-minded trees (people) can intermingle and relate to you and respect your space?

You may need professional help to do all of this. Help is available from many different sources.

You can have this space (this home). A place to set down your roots, a place to grow and develop, but first you must stop wandering aimlessly from place to place.

Affirmation:

I will stand still.

I will create a safe and secure space for myself.

I allow myself to become connected to the earth.

If I feel scared, rejected or unable to cope, I will get help to deal with these issues.

I grow strong and secure.

(47)
Gut Feelings

Gut feelings are the feelings that come from the gut.

You get a gut feeling when something is either right or wrong for you at this moment in time.

Are you in doubt as to whether you follow your gut feelings or whether you allow logic to take over?

Has an incident occurred where the decision you made was based on logic rather than going with your gut feeling and now you regret that decision?

If you learn from any situation it is positive. If you go with your gut feeling and the event does not turn out as you may have wished, it can still be a learning experience. It can still turn out to be a positive result in your overall learning process.

Do you follow your gut feelings or when you get a gut feeling do you then allow logic to take over?

Did you ever stand in a queue in the bank/shop, with about ten people in each line? The line beside you moves quickly, until there are only three people now in that queue. Your gut feeling tells you to stay where you are in the queue you are already in, but logic tells you to move to the shorter line. So you move and stand behind the three people in the shorter queue, only to find that within minutes, the queue you had left had cleared and another queue had formed behind them again. Half an hour later you are still waiting to be served, and wondering whether you should now leave this queue and move across to the other one again. – You did not follow your gut feeling.

As you leave town on a busy afternoon your gut feeling tells you to go home the long way, even though the traffic appears busy on that route. Your logic tells you to go home the short way and avoid all the traffic. So you head home the short way, only to discover there are road works holding up the roadway for two miles.

Your gut feeling comes from "the gut" or solar plexus. If the solar plexus centre is closed down, it is often very difficult to have a good "gut feeling" and carry it through to making an intuitive decision. The gut feeling tells you the wisest decision to make. But the logical mind can step in and override this, so you change your mind only to find out later, sometimes when it is too late, that the "gut feeling" was the correct one to follow all along.

Ask yourself a question that has been bothering you or that you are seeking an answer to.

- Put your hands on each side of your solar plexus (which is between the sternum and the naval).
- Take a deep breath and as you exhale allow the answer to the question to come to you.
- Do not try to make sense of the answer – that is logic.
- Your gut feeling is how you really feel and the answer is to go with the feeling.

Affirmation:

I will learn to trust my gut feelings.

(48)
The Earth Is Your Mother

This story may bring awareness to you of the water you drink, the food you eat and how you discard your waste.

Do you pollute the atmosphere?

Do you live in harmony with Mother Earth?

Are you aware of her wants, her needs, her sadness, her sorrow and grief?

Do you thank her for the provisions she has made for you?

Do you leave it to others to care for Mother Earth or do you feel you are doing your share?

Is your conscience clear when it comes to Mother Earth?

Well done if it is – congratulate yourself.

This is the story of a woman who had many sons and many daughters. This woman brought this family into the world. She provided for them and nurtured them as best she could. She fed them and provided clothing for them.

She planted her garden and she grew her crops. When the crops were ready she reaped them, so her family could have food. She gave them love. She asked nothing in return, only that they in turn by her example would do as she had done.

We will follow the story of one son.

When this particular son left home, he forgot most of what he had learned. He forgot his mother. He forgot himself. He took everything he wanted selfishly. He never appreciated all he had or where it came from.

He ignored the fact that his mother was in want or need. He ignored the fact that she was sad and lonely. He ignored the fact that she was hurt and angry. He ignored the fact that the crops his mother had planted were being ravished and destroyed. He ignored the fact that the land that had provided him with food was now being used for other purposes, greed, money etc., but not for what it had been intended. He ignored all of this and he did not care.

He said, "There are others in the family besides me so why should I bother?"

Why should he bother? He has nothing to gain now (or so he thinks) so he leaves it up to the rest of the family to sort out the problems at home. Of course they in turn leave it up to each other thinking, "The job of looking after mother is for someone else."

Meanwhile his mother is dying. Dying from malnutrition, polluted water, and polluted food. She has been ravaged and raped of all that was hers.

One day awareness dawns on this son. He realises his mother is getting closer to her death in this lifetime. He sees how old and feeble she has become. He looks back and says, "If only I had known how much and how fast mother was deteriorating, I could have done something." This man is now angry, because his mother has been abused and neglected. He chose to believe that the other members of the family were taking responsibility for their part in looking after and protecting their mother. This man has resorted to blaming others. He has not taken responsibility for the part *he* played in the neglect of his mother.

At a deep subconscious level, he *did* know how his mother was being abused, but like so many of us he chose to ignore it, thinking the problems with mother would somehow sort themselves out.

He is so sorry now that he did not observe sooner what was happening to his mother. He now realises his children will never know this mother as he once knew her.

He remembers the green fields he played in as a child. He remembers the fields of golden corn, the sound of the singing lark in the clear morning air, the smell of a freshly mown meadow. He remembers the early morning dew on the grass, the clear blue skies and fresh running water.

He realises that unless he acts *now* these will be no more, not for him, not for his children, and not for his children's children.

The mother, who gave birth to this son, holds out her arms in forgiveness. She welcomes him back, as only a mother can do. She gives him a second chance. She shows him her ravaged fields, her beaten body, the wounds and the scars of hurt and pain.

His mother cries tears of anguish for all the loss and all the betrayal, but she is still ready to forgive. As she cries, her tears help to cleanse her bruised body. She shudders and shakes with her sobs. He stands helplessly looking on finding no way to bring comfort to his mother.

But for her, his being here with her is what matters now. For her, his awareness of her pain is what matters most, because only in the awareness of her pain and in the action he now takes, can he prevent her condition deteriorating beyond recovery. She must go through her pain to give birth again, to believe again and to heal and trust again.

In order to plant and grow her seeds on good soil the old soil must first be cleansed. It is necessary for this mother to go through this pain, in order for life to begin again. Trust and belief were brought about again, not in the return of all her family, but in the raising of awareness and the return of one son. It only takes the awareness of one person, to begin making changes and stop what is happening to the mother.

This mother will need a time of rest, peace and solitude. She has gone through many years of pain and survival, but in order for her growth to begin again she must first rest and heal.

It is I, Solomon who is telling you this story – because

this story is about *you*, yes *you*.

The earth is your mother and you are her son.

Ying and Yang. Male and Female.

(Female) The intuitive side. This is the sensitive side, the nurturing side. (Male) The doer. This is the side that acts, the side that can do something. This is the side that can take action.

There is Yin and Yang in all of us, male and female. We all have the ability to feel and act, but in knowing, we have the choice of when and how we act.

Today ask yourself, "How aware are you of what is happening to Mother Earth?"

Ask yourself, "What changes you can make, no matter how small, which can be of help to Mother Earth's survival?

Try to become more aware of all of nature, the air, the rivers, the lakes, the fish, the animals, the birds, the trees, etc.

No matter how little you do – it does make a difference.

Affirmation:

I will become more aware of Mother Earth.

I will live in peace and harmony with Mother Earth.

(49)
Forgiveness Of Your Inner Child

This is about forgiveness of your inner child.

Do you have a problem with forgiveness?

Some may say yes, others may say no.

What about you?

Do *you* find it difficult or easy to forgive yourself?

At some early age you may have done something, which you may still feel guilty about. You may have been only four years of age at the time when you pushed your baby brother, injuring him. Now every time you see his scar, you feel guilty, not to a great degree, but still nonetheless you may feel an element of guilt.

Another example, you may have witnessed something hurtful physical or emotional been inflicted on someone else, and have felt powerless and helpless at the time, and unable to do anything to stop it. You may have been only six years of age at the time. The victim may have been a child of three and the perpetrator an adult.

At a later stage in life you hear how particular acts or deeds inflicted on a child, can affect them for the rest of their lives. You now as an adult may start to remember an incident or incidents, when something like this happened. You may start to regret not having done something about it. Remember you were only six years of age at that time, and could not have done anything about what was happening.

Remember a child's mind is global. By this we mean that the child feels responsible for all that has happened. However the adult may now find they have difficulty distinguishing between the adult guilt, and the guilt they experienced as a child. What can happen however is that the adult has not forgiven the child within.

This child may have witnessed a hurtful deed of physical, emotional or sexual abuse. They did not participate in this deed. They may have been mentally crippled with fear of the possible consequences, if they told someone about what had happened. Remember the child may feel they themselves are bad, because of what has happened. They may believe this for many years and sometimes right throughout their lives.

But how do we as adults, forgive the child within for what the child has or has not done?

Can you imagine yourself living in a beautiful house? You are the house. Your girlfriend comes visiting you for the first time. You answer the door and invite her in. Everywhere is immaculate except for one thing. In the corner of the room you have a cage and in that cage is a forty-year-old man. Your girlfriend looks at you and back at the man in the cage, and eventually asks you why this man is locked up. You tell her that he saw something very bad and did not do anything about it. When she asks you what he could have done about it you reply, "Physically, there was nothing he could have done when it happened, because he was just a child of six and the perpetrator was an adult, however," you say, "He should have told someone else about it, even though he was only six at the time." She now says, "You are punishing a boy of six for over thirty years." "Yes," you reply, "How can I forgive him?"

This girl feels a cold shiver and thinks to herself "Today was the day I had intended to share some painful secrets with this man, but if he cannot show forgiveness for a six year old boy, who had no control over an incident that happened over thirty years ago, how can he possibly have empathy or show compassion for me as an adult?"

She says "I have spent so many years coping and dealing with many issues, traumas etc., that have occurred in my life. I have spent many years trying to come to terms with, deal, and heal from what happened to me as a child. Through therapy I am learning forgiveness of my inner child. If this man cannot show forgiveness of his own inner child (a child of only six), how can he possibly understand or show compassion for my inner child?"

Today, try and take some time out for yourself. Ask yourself, have you been punishing your inner child? Have you been feeling guilty and responsible and punishing yourself, for events that have happened in the past, events that were beyond your control and for which you were not responsible?

Remember the child is never guilty. If you have been punishing your inner child, you may need to learn forgiveness of that little child within. This may take time, care and nurturing.

You may need professional help to get in touch with your inner child:

A child waiting to be re-born.

A child waiting to be accepted.

A child waiting to be free.

A child who can only be freed by you.

A child who can only be forgiven by you.

Affirmation:

I give freedom to my inner child.

I accept my inner child.

I heal my inner child.

I am my inner child.

I am me.

(50)
The Well

The well is symbolic of the Self. The water in the well symbolises all you have in life.

Have you checked up on your life's resources recently?

How are you feeling today?

Do you feel full of life?

Do you feel full of energy?

Are you bursting at the seams and overflowing with all you have to give?

Are you overflowing with love, joy and abundance, or do you have little or nothing more left for yourself or anyone else?

Each and every one of us has our own supply of life's resources. This could be likened to a well, the fountain of life or the spring of life.

Have you looked into your well recently? (Looked at your life, your way of being)?

How much water is in your well? Is it almost drained dry, practically empty? (Do you feel your health or your life is being drained away)?

How clean is the water in your well? Is it sparkling, healthy and free flowing, going with the flow of life, or is it dull, polluted and stagnant? (Is your physical body free from toxins and pollutants)?

Is your emotional body free from emotional and mental baggage?

When you look in your well is the water clear? (Can you look at yourself and see clearly what is going on within)?

Do you feel you have enough water left for the remainder of your journey "your life?" (Is your well overflowing with plenty of life's resources; love, happiness, joy, good food etc.)?

Have you been living your life to its full potential, or has your well dried up from lack of use? Have you been relying on others for your supply of life's resources (health, happiness, fun, joy etc.)?

Has your well clogged up because you have allowed others to dump their rubbish in it (emotional, physical and mental rubbish)? Have you been allowing the dumping of rubbish on your being, (blocking your life's resources)? Have you yourself been dumping rubbish in your well (poor diet, little exercise)? Has this dumping caused you ill health?

Are you down to a trickle of water, barely enough for you to survive? (Are you just about coping with life)? Are you allowing other people to take water from your well without your prior permission? Did you explain to them that it was necessary to ask *you* first if they wanted water from your well?

Have you encouraged others to find their own tools for their survival (activate their own wells), or did *you* do it for them, not allowing them to learn for themselves? Have you given water (time, money etc.) to people who had no regard for where it came from and so discarded it indiscriminately (no value on you or your resources)?

Have you kept your well serviced and in a good state of repair. Have you kept your body, mind and spirit healthy? Does it sometimes make you feel good when others depend on you for their very existence, even at a cost to you and your health?

Only when you learn to activate your own well and keep it clean and topped up, can you help others to do the same. You cannot take anyone where you haven't been.

What can you do now?

You can become more aware and say "no" when you realise rubbish is being dumped in your well. You can learn to create stronger boundaries around your well to prevent any more rubbish being dumped in it. You may need to do this before it blocks your well completely.

You can become more aware of how, when and by whom your well is being drained. You can learn to check your well on a regular basis (by getting regular health checks). You can learn not to give away water indiscriminately. You can learn it is not your responsibility to satisfy the needs of others. You can learn you do not need to be thirsty (ill) before checking your supply of water (your health).

You can learn it is only when your own well is full or overflowing, that you can really afford to give water away and then only to someone who needs it to survive until they can activate their own supply of water. (Until they can find the resources they need to survive on their own).

It is never too late to check your well. (It is never too late to check your life's resources).

Today ask your guides, your God, your angels to help you lift the lid on your well (your life).

Take a peek inside – do not be afraid.

Everything you need to activate and clean out your well, if needed, is available to you for the asking.

With your new awareness you will be able to make any necessary changes. Awareness does not go away, it brings freedom – freedom of choice and freedom to be.

Affirmation:

I will check my life's resources.

I will not be afraid to say "no" to those who are dumping their rubbish in my well.

I will create and maintain strong boundaries to protect my resources.

I will not give away water indiscriminately.

I will allow and encourage others to activate their own life's resources.

I will take care of and cherish the resources that have been given to me for my life.

(51)
Responsibility

Do you feel laden down and overburdened with responsibility?

Do you feel life itself is a burden for you?

Do you feel that you have been taking responsibility for other people and now it has become too much for you?

Do you realise you are not responsible for anyone but yourself?

If you have children in your care you have a responsibility to them and their needs. What you say or do will have an affect on their lives, but you cannot take full responsibility for their behaviour. They will have learned behaviours, learned from parents, peers, friends and society. They will apply this behaviour when circumstances trigger a memory where they have applied similar behaviours in the past, and where those behaviours were effective for them.

You are responsible for everything you say and do, but you are not responsible for another person's reactions.

***Their* reaction is based on *their* past.**

Everything that has happened to you up to this moment has created the person you are in this moment. However, how you behave in this moment, is creating the person you will be in the next moment.

- Living in the moment is so important because you are creating the "you" for tomorrow.
- You cannot change the past.
- The future is only a possibility.

- There is only the moment – this moment.
- You are not responsible for anyone but yourself.

Today ask yourself, are you trying to take responsibility for someone else's behaviour? If so it may be time to stand back and allow them their learnings.

The next time think before jumping and problem solving.

Take a deep breath and ask yourself, "Is this good for me?" "Is this good for the person I am trying to take responsibility for?"

Is there something you need to learn?

Is there some past behaviour patterns you need to look at?

Affirmation:

Take a deep breath and repeat:

I will only take responsibility for my own actions and behaviours.

(52)
Don't Be Fooled By Me

Don't be fooled by me.

Don't be fooled by the face I wear, for I wear a thousand masks. Masks that I am afraid to take off, and none of them is me.

Pretending is an art that's second nature to me, but don't be fooled, for Heaven's sake don't be fooled.

I give the impression that I'm secure, that the water's calm, I'm in command, and I need no one, but please don't believe me.

My surface may seem smooth, but my surface is my mask. Beneath this lies my complacence. Beneath dwells the real me in confusion, in fear, and aloneness, but I hide this. I don't want anybody to know it.

I panic at the thought of my weakness and fear being exposed. That's why I frantically create a mask to hide behind, a nonchalant, sophisticated facade, to help me pretend, to shield me from the glance that knows, but such a glance is precisely my salvation. My only salvation, and I know it. That is, if it's followed by acceptance, if it's followed by love. It's the only thing that will assure me of what I can't assure myself, that I'm worth something.

But I don't tell you this. I don't dare. I'm afraid to. I'm afraid your glance will not be followed by acceptance, and love.

I'm afraid you'll think less of me that you'll laugh at me, and your laugh would kill me.

I'm afraid that deep down I'm nothing, that I'm no good, and that you will see this and reject me.

So I play my game, my desperate game, with a facade of assurance without, and a trembling child within.

And so begins the parade of masks, and my life becomes a front.

I idly chatter to you in suave tones of surface talk. I tell you everything is really nothing, and nothing of what's everything, of what's crying within me. So, when I'm going through my routine, do not be fooled by what I'm saying.

Please listen carefully and try and hear what I'm not saying, what I'd like to be able to say, what for survival I need to say, but what I can't say.

Don't be fooled by me.

*Author unknown.

(53)
The Jail

You may be on the receiving end of a controlling situation or a controlling person.

You may be the perpetrator of a controlling situation and are attempting to control others.

If neither of those statements are true at the moment, is it possible there was a time in the past when you were in either or both of those situations?

If so what have you learned?

How many of us have built jails in our lives?

How many keys to how many jails do we hold in our hands?

We may have started to build these jails from the moment we were born. How many keys to how many lives are we now holding? How many prisoners do we have in our jails, (husbands, wives, partners, boyfriends, girlfriends, children, parents, friends, relatives, employers, or employees)? You may have your physical jails and you may have your emotional jails.

Does this story relate to you?

Do you let some of your prisoners out of your jail on the odd occasion? (Do you allow your family and friends freedom only whenever *you* choose)? Do you hold others in your jail for a lifetime? (Do you try to control some people throughout their entire lives)?

Do you make the jail sentence for some of your prisoners "a living hell?"(Do you force your opinions and your belief systems on others? Do you try to manipulate and control others without any regard for their health or well-being)?

Do you put other prisoners in cells that are barely habitable, cramped and unhealthy? (Do you inflict cramped and unhealthy living conditions on those in your care)? Do you keep the keys to the cells on a long chain, so you can release your prisoners for short periods of time and pull them back whenever you choose? (Do you have many lives at the end of a long chain, lives that you can control and restrain whenever you choose)? Are you afraid if you allow your prisoners their freedom, they may discover new learnings, new ways of being? This could mean, you will no longer be in control of them or their lives.

Are you afraid that if you allow your family their freedom and their learnings, they will no longer have a need for you? Do you make your jail so comfortable, that your prisoners may feel guilty if they leave? They may feel indebted to you, for taking responsibility for them and their behaviour.

When you grant your prisoners a day's leave, do you put a long chain around them so they do not ramble too far? (When your partner, child or friend decides to take some time out away from you, do you make it impossible for them to wander too far, or stay away too long)? Do you put restrictions on their time, their finance etc., so they will have to return to you whenever *you* decide they should?

We all play the part of the jailor from time to time. We also play the part of the prisoner from time to time.

Take a dysfunctional marriage for example.

One partner may refuse to agree to end the relationship, because it will allow the other person to go free. One person may attempt to stop or curtail the other person's freedom, by withholding finance, refusing to sign agreements or by aggressive, manipulative or controlling behaviour. Both of these people are in jail. They are both playing a part.

Take a job for example. One person may refuse to leave, in case it opens up opportunities and gives options to others. (The jailer will not leave in case the prisoners escape and have their freedom. Their freedom of choice).

Have you been a jailer at times throughout your life?

How often do you hold people to a particular way of being or doing, regardless of their circumstances? How often maybe as a parent do you hold your children to promises, which they have made to you, but are now unable to keep? How often do you expect your families to do what is beyond their capabilities? When they grow older, perhaps with families of their own, you may expect them to call on a particular day at a particular time, regardless of their health, well-being or family circumstances. (As children we may also do this to our parents).

You may have the key to their emotional needs. (It could possibly be a need to be praised or accepted). You hold the key to their prison. Do you let them out, for only as long as you see fit?

What about freedom, freedom of choice, freedom to be, free will?

Ask yourself the question, "Are you in jail?"

How often does your jailer make promises of wealth, property etc., for instance to a son, daughter, parent, partner, relation or employee, just to hold or tie them to a family, company, land or business?

You are in jail – but so are they.

How often does your jailer make promises "for when you retire?" How often does the prisoner stay on best behaviour and live in hope of an early release, or that his jailer would move on, only to discover on the day that he is released, that there was never a lock on his door in the first place. He had the choice at all times whether to stay or go. – He had free will at all times – What a waste of a lifetime!

What are you afraid of if you give someone his or her freedom? Are you afraid they will go away and never return? Are you afraid that you are the one who will feel alone? Are you afraid of the choices they will make? Or are you afraid, that the choices they make may not include you?

How many of our children leave home, only to return unable to cope with the traumas and stresses of life outside "our prison?" Prison is the only reality they know. How many of us leave dysfunctional jobs or relationships, only to return to the same or similar circumstances and situations at a later stage?

Does it make *you* feel good that your children continually return home to you, so *you* can sort out their problems? As your children grow older, do you allow them to take care of their own health and well-being? Do you impose your laws and regulations on them, as to how and where they should live their lives? Remember we have a responsibility to our children, but we are not responsible for anyone but ourselves.

Do you give them limited information, not because you do not have it to give, but because if you give unlimited knowledge or freedom they may not come back?

Do you teach and inform your children how to avail of life's resources, or do you deny them their learnings by supplying them with all their wants and needs? If your children do not learn how to cope with life and resolve life's issues, they will continually return to you, not for direction or help, but so that you resolve their problems for them.

It may not seem like it on the surface, but these are all forms of control, which we learn in order to keep our children, families or friends in our prisons.

Do not forget that as long as you have held or try to hold another human being in captivity, you are also in jail. You are a prisoner in your own jail, and you are also the jailer. You created your prison to hold others, forgetting that you would also be in captivity as long as you held prisoners.

You hold the key.

You hold the key to their freedom and you hold the key to your own freedom. You may think you are *not* holding anyone in captivity, or that you yourself are not in captivity, but with the use of control, power, manipulation and sometimes selfish kindness, you can make it virtually impossible for someone to leave you, or for you yourself to leave your jail.

Like the king in a later story you too may also be in a position to offer someone their freedom. Freedom to think for themselves. Freedom to live. Freedom to be.

You create your reality, whether you are the jailer or the prisoner.

You are the prisoner of your own thoughts, your own conditioning, and your own reality, but you can never create a reality for another. When things become unbearable, when this prison and the prisoners in it are destroying everything you have, your health and your entire being, you may ask your God or your guides for help. When the guides send help it can come in many ways. Help does not always come in the way you might expect it. It could be an article you read in a magazine or paper. It could be a book you borrow or buy, or someone may give it to you as a present. It could be something someone says to you, or perhaps you may receive some guidance from a seminar or workshop you may attend. It could come via therapy. It could simply be a "thought out of the blue," that may start you on the road to a new way of looking at your life and your situation.

Fear can prevent you from escaping.

When you are in this situation, resembling a prisoner in jail, and you are holding on to the bars of your cell because of a fear of letting go, what can you do?

First of all you must let go of the bars, before you can even contemplate freedom. (Let go of conditioning. Let go of old belief systems). Let go of the bars of your prison so that the gate may be opened. You must "let go" of the safety of being in captivity, so you can see the sunlight. Every day that you live without sunlight, without nourishment, without love or without freedom is a day too many. As a jailer you must also let go. Let go and hand over the keys of your jail. Let go of your need to control. Let go of your prisoners. You do have the choice.

Free yourself.

Time is not on your side. The time for freedom is now. Only when you are free can you free those around you. When you are free, you can live in harmony and in peace with your fellow men.

In captivity your life is spent thinking about freedom. A prisoner may even choose to die rather than spend a lifetime in prison. With freedom you have choice. This is either to return to captivity or to remain free.

You must have and give freedom:

Freedom to make choices.

Freedom to be as you want to be.

Freedom to ask for help.

Freedom to accept help.

There are those who would prefer to stay in prison (stay in a situation, job, family or relationship), because to be released from captivity and have freedom would mean taking on the responsibility of surviving outside the prison, perhaps for the first time in their lives.

Solomon tells a story about a King and his Son:

There was a king who had one son. The son in material terms had everything he could ever want for. Every wish he had was granted. As this son grew older, he begged his father for freedom. Freedom to leave the castle. Freedom to follow his own path in life.

So one day his father said, "You may go." As soon as the father's words were spoken, the son felt panic, because in those words he understood what freedom really meant.

Freedom meant:

Taking responsibility for himself and for everything he said and did.

Freedom to choose.

Freedom simply to "be."

The son left the castle and started leading his own life. He then realised freedom was not what he really wanted. He did not really want to make choices. He did not really want to take responsibility for himself or his actions.

He wanted freedom without responsibility.

Solomon tells the story about a slave:

The master has a slave tied at the end of a long rope. The slave seeks and begs for freedom. The master suddenly decides to cut the rope and give him his freedom. For a while the slave stumbles and falls, and then gets up and staggers around for a while. He then stands and realises he is free. The next thing he does is run away as far as he possibly can.

Eventually he stops and looks around him and wonders to himself:

"What happens next?"

"Where do I eat?"

"Where do I sleep?"

"Where do I work?"

Now he realises what having freedom means, – it means taking responsibility.

Responsibility for his work.

Responsibility to provide his own food.

Responsibility for his living conditions.

Responsibility for his health.

Responsibility for himself.

Solomon tells the story about a dog:

This story is about a dog continually barking to get out of his shed. So you open the door, the dog rushes out, he turns around, looks back and then goes back and sits on the doorstep.

Solomon gives a further image of a bird in a cage:

The bird is fluttering around all day trying to get out. You open the cage door to find the bird flies only a few feet away from the cage. He then flies back to rest on top of the cage. At least he has choice now that he has been given his freedom.

- Release your prisoners: People, friends, relations, employers, employees.
- Knock down your jail: Old belief systems, conditioning, fears.

Only you can knock down your jails, because it was you who built them. When you do this, you are free to come and go as you please, and so are they. They are free and so are you. Free to allow the universal energies to deal with and help each and every one of us as they see fit.

We long for freedom at all times, but when and if we get it, it may sometimes be too late. The ability of the prisoner to adapt to new circumstances, to think for themselves, and to face the challenges of life, may all seem insurmountable, following many years in isolation and away from the learning experiences of life outside the jail.

When you look more closely, there may not have been any bars on your windows. There may not have been any locks on your doors. There may not have been any jailor preventing you from leaving at any time. You may have been a prisoner of your own thoughts, conditioning and beliefs. You may have been a prisoner of someone else's thoughts, conditioning and beliefs.

Do not judge yourself too harshly. You may have been

working without awareness, and with the only knowledge you had at the time.

With awareness you can make changes.

You can give freedom to your prisoners.

You can give freedom to yourself.

Affirmation:

I am free.

I give freedom.

(54)
Do You Feel Lost?

Are you feeling lost?

Do you feel you do not know which way to turn?

Do you feel you have gone astray?

Do you feel you may have wandered off your path?

Were you travelling on what you thought to be the right road, or did you have a nagging feeling in your gut, that you had gone astray somewhere along the way?

- Can you remember how long ago it was, when you first got this feeling?
- How far back on your journey did you feel you were gone or going astray?
- At what stage of your journey did you fail to recognise the signs (the warnings)?

Did you keep on going; regardless of the fact you knew you were completely lost?

Did you genuinely not notice the warning signs, or did you see them, but chose to ignore them?

Did you notice the signs that said:

- **Road flooded** – Have you been taking too much on board, especially other people's problems and issues?
- **Dangerous bends. Slow down** – Did you slow down and take care of yourself, your health, and your general well-being?
- **Road works ahead. Prepare to stop** – Did you run slap bang into the road works (crisis) or were you able to stop in time?

These are some of the obstacles you encountered in life. Some were meant to slow you down or stop you temporarily. Did you drive through these obstacles regardless of the consequences? Did you use means to get through your difficult times, that were not always healthy or positive i.e. drink, drugs, addictive or dysfunctional behaviour?

- **White line. Do not cross** – Did you cross this line, breaking boundaries, trespassing on other people's space, not recognising your own or other people's boundaries?
- **Crossroads ahead** – Did you reach a crossroads in your life, where it was necessary for you to make major decisions? Did you ignore those decisions and allow someone else to decide for you? You may not have known which way to turn at the crossroads, and so allowed someone else to decide which way you should go. Did you go straight through the crossroads believing that you would eventually find your way?

When you found you were completely lost:

- Did you stop, get out of the car (situation) and take a look around you?
- Did you ask for help?
- Did you ask for directions?
- Did you continue to drive aimlessly around going from place to place (from friends to your doctor to neighbours etc.) never knowing where you were going and not knowing where you would end up? You may have been burning up fuel, wearing out your car (burning up your life's resources, wearing yourself out, going nowhere, with very little to show for your life).
- Were you travelling so fast that you did not see any signs or any obstacles?
- Do you need to crash in order for you to stop? (Do you need to crash physically, emotionally or mentally in

order for you to stop)?

Your journey may have started with indecision, (indecisive parents, indecisive teachers, not having a sense of direction themselves).

- Were the directions you did receive during childhood, clear, or confusing?
- Did you feel at different stages of your journey, that you were not heading in the right direction?
- Is it possible that the journey you travelled was based on conditioning? Conditioning says, "Do not ask why. Do not show fear. Do not ask questions. Keep going at all costs."
- Do you have difficulty in admitting you may have made a mistake or taken a wrong turn (a mistake in the road you chose)?
- Did you allow a fellow traveller to lead you astray?

You may have now reached a point on your journey where you feel tired and exhausted. You may have worked with the only knowledge you had in the past.

It is what you do now that is important. If you have learned even one small lesson from your journey then it is positive. You cannot go back. You cannot change the past, but you can learn from it.

You can use the learnings from your past journey to enable you to have a more positive, safe and healthy journey in the future. But first you must stop.

Whenever you feel lost – stop. Take a deep breath and ask yourself:

- Where am I?
- Where am I going?
- Where do I want to go?

- Is this journey for my greater good?
- What type of fellow travellers would I like to share my journey with?

Go with your gut feelings rather than conditioning.

We all get lost from time to time. Do not be afraid to ask for directions. There is no road that has not been travelled before. We all come to a crossroads, at some stage of our journey through life. It is not how fast you get through it, – it is "how" you get through it and what you learn on the way.

What can you do whenever you decide to commence a new journey?

- Give yourself permission to use all the new tools, new learnings and techniques you have acquired and developed.
- Give yourself permission to ask for help and directions.
- If you feel you are being misled give yourself permission to say "no." Most of all give yourself permission to learn from your experiences. With your experiences and learnings from life, you could be a signpost for someone else on their journey.

You may be feeling a bit battered and worn out from your journey so far, but give yourself credit you *have* survived it.

Affirmation:

I will become more aware of the signposts on my journey.

I will learn to stop when I feel I have gone astray.

I will seek directions when I feel lost.

I ask my God, my guides, my angels to guide me on my journey.

(55)
Potholes

This story is about how you learn from life's experiences. It is about the choices you can make in life.

Do you learn from life's experiences?

Do you sometimes say to yourself when you have repeated a pattern that did not work for you in the past, –"Will I ever learn?"

Do you learn from life or do you continue with old behaviour patterns, hurting and punishing yourself and sometimes hurting and punishing those around you, your family, friends and colleagues?

Are you learning from your experiences and making the necessary changes to create a happy, healthy and balanced life?

You do have choices in your life and in how you learn.

Imagine every evening on your way home from work when it is generally dark, you run into a pothole damaging your car tyre. Then every morning you get out of bed to discover you have a flat tyre. At this stage, you notice that the rim of your wheel is also damaged. Because of all of this you are late for work again. You are also annoyed and frustrated. You do not know where the pothole is. You do not have the time or energy to go looking for it. You hope that maybe someone else will discover it, fix it, fill it in or repair it. This pothole may not be bothering anyone else. Nobody else may be aware of it.

One day you discover exactly where the pothole is. Even at this point you do have a choice.

1. You could fill in the pothole.

2. You could go home a different way.
3. You could get someone else to fill in the pothole.
4. You could avoid the pothole.
5. You could change your place of work.

Where are the potholes in your life?

- Are there aspects of your life bothering you and causing you pain? Are you having difficulty finding the cause let alone deal with it?
- Is there someone or something delaying you on your journey through life? When you realise what is causing this delay (your obstacles, discomforts and pains) you then have choices, regarding what means you may use to resolve or repair them.

At all times you do have choices.

Imagine every morning you hurt your hand as you pass through the kitchen door, and every evening you pass back through the same door hurting your hand again. What can you do to prevent yourself from being hurt? Do you avoid the door altogether? Do you leave the kitchen using a different door? Do you stop to examine the door? It could be just a loose screw, or the door could be about to fall on you or somebody else causing serious injury.

Avoiding issues in life does not resolve them. Nothing changes if you do not change that which is causing you hurt or pain. How much pain and inconvenience do you need to experience, before you take action? Do not expect that someone else is going to resolve your problem. They may not be even aware that there is a problem, and if they are aware, it may not be hurting or inconveniencing *them* in any way.

What do you need to do to make changes in your working life, marriage, family or relationships? Small potholes could be occurring, without your awareness. It is only when they become bigger or cause inconvenience, pain or hurt, that you may sometimes become aware of them.

Today is the day when you need to look at the potholes in your life.

- Look at your potholes.
- Look at what or who is causing you pain.
- Look at the choices available to you.
- Get help if you need to fill in your potholes. If there are potholes affecting your life, do not deny that they are there.

Reward yourself no matter how little for your awareness and your courage in dealing with your potholes.

Affirmation:

Today I will examine the potholes in my life.

I have many choices in how I can deal with the potholes in my life.

I will make the appropriate changes to deal with the potholes in my life.

(56)
Don't Hit The Ball Back

Do you play games, physical, emotional or mental?

What do you do when you are in a situation where there are constant arguments and disagreements, which never seem to end?

Do you always have to have the last word or do you let it go?

What can you do when someone is constantly "pressing your buttons" in an inappropriate or unacceptable manner, i.e. making comments which they know you will react to, especially if it concerns you or someone close to you, or issues you may have a strong belief about, or opinion on?

What can you do when someone is constantly "pressing your buttons" by continually picking arguments with you over what are seemingly minor issues?

What can you do when someone is constantly criticising you or the work you do, criticising your family, friends, morals, belief system or ethics?

See this ongoing scenario like a game of tennis. How do you stop playing a game that you do not like, that is neither healthy or enjoyable for you? If you engage in unhealthy game playing with another person, it may be harmful for you physically, emotionally and mentally.

How do you stop this game playing?

The answer is simple – Don't hit the ball back!

The next time this person hits the ball to you (angry words, criticism etc.) the ball will be in your court. Look at the ball (listen to the angry words, criticisms etc). Take a deep breath and ask yourself:

- Do I want to play this game anymore?
- Are there any learnings for me in this game?
- Am I wasting valuable time playing a game where there are little or no learnings for me?

What can you do next?

First of all you can restrain yourself (hold your tongue).

Don't hit the ball back!

Your part of the game will now have ended.

You may express to this person that you do not feel like playing this game anymore. It may be difficult for you to walk away. Habit is a very difficult thing to break. You do have a choice at all times whether you continue to play this game or not.

The other player also has a choice whether to stop or continue playing this game with you. If they wish to continue the game, and you do not wish to play with them, it is *their* choice whether they seek out a new partner, who *will* play their game.

The next time the ball is in your court, no matter who has hit it or how hard it has been hit, take a deep breath. Ask yourself, "Is this game good for me?" If it is not, – then let it go. Don't hit the ball back. You do have the choice, to find another court with a new partner and play a game best suited to your needs.

Today take note of situations where you have difficulty "holding your tongue." There is a difference between expressing your feelings and engaging in unhealthy game playing.

Affirmation:

I will choose the game that is best suited to my needs.

I will choose the partner with whom I will have the greatest learnings.

I will choose the games in life, which are best suited for my evolvement.

I will learn to distinguish between expressing how I feel, and prolonging an argument (tit for tat game playing).

I will learn when *not* to hit the ball back.

(57)
Types Of Fear

Is fear controlling your life?

Do you feel fearful?

Do you have an unknown sense of fear?

Do you know the cause of your fear?

Do you have fear of fear?

Fear is like a raging mad dog locked in a shed.

The dog can control you in the same way that fear does. You are afraid to open the door, because you are not sure what is really inside. You can hear the noise, you can hear the barking, but the longer you listen and do nothing and the longer it goes on, the worse it becomes.

How big is the dog? The longer he is locked up, the bigger he becomes *in your mind.* However, if you allow the dog out, you can at least see how big or small this dog really is. You are afraid to let the dog out and like fear you keep it locked up. But if you let out this dog (this fear), you can at least confront him. It is what he might do, that creates the fear. Fear locked in becomes greater and greater, but when you allow the fear out and confront it, it then loses its power.

Types of fear to name just a few:

Fear of loss, fear of not having enough, fear of failure, fear of success, fear of change, fear of letting go, fear of illness, fear of being close (in case of loss), fear of trust, fear of fear.

- When loss is experienced, especially of someone close, fear of loss can create a fear of trust in case we lose again.
- Fear of not having enough can cause a hoarding pat-

tern, holding on to anything whether it be of value or not. It can also cause greed.

- Fear of failure can prevent us from moving forward and being successful.
- Fear of success can cause us to hold back on job promotion etc., because of the pressure and responsibility it may entail.
- Fear of change can stop us moving on, expanding and taking on life's challenges.
- Fear of letting go can cause a holding pattern. Holding on to our outdated belief systems, holding on to jobs, properties, families and relationships that are no longer of any learning value to us.
- Fear of trust: When trust has been broken we may have a fear of trusting again.

Are you being controlled by fear?

Are you controlling through fear?

Affirmation:

I will not allow myself to be controlled by fear.

I will not allow myself to control others through fear.

(58)
Acting On Assumptions

Can assumptions sometimes be a source of annoyance to you or to others?

Do you make assumptions and then act on those assumptions? Can this be a source of annoyance to other people or can it have a positive outcome?

Do people make assumptions about you from time to time? Do they make assumptions about where you are going, what you are doing, what you may be doing, or where you may be going?

Do they sometimes act on those assumptions?

Are the assumptions sometimes correct and at other times incorrect?

We all make assumptions from time to time. As children we assume that we will have enough to eat and drink and enough love to survive. We assume our parents will take good care of us physically, emotionally, and mentally, and that they will also ensure that we get a good education, and following that, a good job. As adults we assume that if we work hard enough, we will be rewarded and get adequately paid for the work we do.

Assumptions do not allow for human behaviour or error. When we act on assumptions we can sometimes come up against a number of problems. Humans are not predictable. Their actions and emotions are governed by life's experiences both past and present.

We can make assumptions about the regular opening hours of our local petrol station, and if we call there for petrol and the sign says "Open" we are right to assume we will get petrol. Taking human behaviour into account the petrol attendant may have finished work and forgotten to switch off the

"Open" sign and turn on the "Closed" sign. But if we act on the assumption that we *will* get petrol, even though the person in the last car that drove out told us the station was closed, we could waste hours waiting for the petrol attendant to come back.

On the other hand if someone says to you "Joe I am not feeling well, I have got terrible chest pains." You may possibly assume he is going to have a heart attack and act on this assumption. You take him to hospital where he does have a heart attack, – so you assumed correctly. You assumed and acted upon something that could have saved this man's life. You may have acted this way because you had an experience in the past, where someone close to you died because action was not taken fast enough, – in this case you have assumed correctly.

Supposing your next-door neighbour is out cutting the lawn and cuts his finger with the lawnmower. You cut your finger last week doing a similar job, but you were okay, so you assume that your neighbour is also okay. He is looking very pale and losing blood. He asks you to take him to the hospital, but you convince him it is not necessary to seek medical attention, based on your own experience last week. You are now acting on an assumption. You discover a week later that this man has a serious infection. – Your assumption here was incorrect.

Supposing you walk into a bar and you assume by the way a certain individual is looking at you, that he is going to hit you. This poor man may have a problem with his sight, and he is trying to figure out if he knows you or not. You act on your assumptions and go and hit him first, only to find this man had no ill will towards you at all. – You are now acting on an assumption that is incorrect.

You may assume someone is hungry and prepare a meal for them after their long journey, but you did not ask them if they had eaten or not. You assumed because of the early morning drive, that nowhere would be open, only to find, that they had eaten a meal at the new 24 hour restaurant, which had opened up along the route. – You have now wasted a lot of time and money on an assumption.

We assume someone will or will not do something, judging by the way we ourselves would behave in similar circumstances. We are not this person. We are not allowing them to ask for or tell us, what they want, or what their needs are. Our experience may be similar, but never the same.

How many times have you said, "I assumed you would be there?"

- We do not have the right to assume for someone else, no more than they have the right to assume for us.
- We must learn when to act on assumptions and when not to act on assumptions.
- We need to allow others to explain or tell us what they want or do not want.
- We may have similar experiences, but every person's individual reaction to a similar situation, is based on their past experiences and how they themselves dealt with issues in the past.
- We can never assume that another individual will act or react as we do.
- We can never assume that the needs of others will be the same as our needs. We do not have that right.

Affirmation:

I will endeavour to find out the true fact about a person or situation rather than act on an assumption.

(59)
Allowing Free Will

Do you allow others their freedom of choice or do you manipulate others for your own benefit?

Are you aware that at all times you have free will?

Are you aware that other people have free will at all times?

Have you ever been in a situation where someone tried to interfere with your free will?

Have you ever found that you yourself tried to interfere with someone else's free will?

Have you ever tried to impose your will on others, and a situation developed where it ended in disaster?

Do you impose your will on others or do you allow free will?

If you are on your way to a football game and you see your neighbour on the other side of the road walking in the opposite direction, what would you do? Would you cross the road and say, "How are you Jack? Did you hear about the big game that is on today? Would you like to come? I'm on my way there and my car is just around the corner."

Jack may hesitate and say "I would love to come to the game, but I promised the kids I would take them to the cinema."

Do you now persist, by telling Jack that he should leave the kids and their film until the following week and come to the game with you, as it is going to be a great game?

Jack then replies that he would like to come, but he has not got enough money with him. You tell him not to worry about money, that you will pay for the tickets to the game. Jack now hesitates, but is seriously considering your proposition. You then tell him you will take him home immediately after the game is over. He agrees to go. – Jack is won over.

You both go to the game and you pay for Jack's ticket. After the game, you are joined by friends who insist you join them for a drink. Knowing he is short of money, you tell Jack that you will pay for his drinks, if he will come along. Jack goes along to the bar for drinks with you and your friends. By now he feels he has lost control of his own destiny. He feels indebted to you and that it would be ungracious of him to be disagreeable, and either way, it is too late to go back home and take the kids to the cinema.

For Jack a sense of hopelessness and anxiety has now set in. He anticipates the inevitable row when he gets home and the look of disappointment on his children's faces. "But why worry about all this now," he thinks, "I might as well get drunk." And so he does and gets totally ossified. He refuses to leave the bar at closing time. He knocks over a few tables, spilling his own and other people's drinks, and then becomes quite aggressive with the barperson.

What can you do with Jack now?

He has now become a burden on you. He refuses to go home and you feel you cannot go home without him. You feel responsible for him and you also feel you owe him something for bringing him here in the first place.

Go back to what happened for you when you first told Jack about the game. Were you experiencing a need to take on a passenger and then control him, so he would owe you one? Did you think you knew what was best for Jack? You may have thought you were doing him a favour. Instead you tried to impose your will on Jack, but you ended up being controlled by Jack's subsequent behaviour.

What could you have done?

- You could have told Jack there was a game on and you were going to it.

- You could have asked him if he would like to come with you.
- You could have listened to Jack when he said he had other arrangements.

You must ask yourself what was going on for you when you insisted on Jack going to the game?

- Do you have difficulty taking "no" for an answer?
- Do you override another person's needs, by inflicting *your* opinions and *your* beliefs on them?
- Is this a power struggle for you?

Does this story sound familiar?

Is there any resemblance between this story and a situation you have found yourself in?

Remember you are responsible for yourself and your behaviour, but you are not responsible for the other person's reaction to it.

The law of the universe is non-interference.

The next time you find yourself in a similar situation, take a deep breath and ask yourself, is there a need within you to control others?

Remember in trying to control others, you may end up being the one that is being controlled.

How can you change?

Stop manipulating (if this is what you are doing).

Stop trying to force your will on somebody (if this is what you are doing).

Affirmation:

I will think before I speak or act.

I will ask myself why I am saying what it is I am saying.

I will ask myself why I am doing what it is I am doing.

I will ask myself what is the *real motive* behind what I say or what I do.

I will recognise and respect the free will of others.

I will learn that everyone has free will.

(60)
How We Lose

Do you feel you have lost someone or something?

There are times in our lives when we may feel we have lost something or someone who is important to us. We may feel we need to find this special something or someone in order to make our lives complete again.

- Do you feel lost or alone?
- Do you feel you have been abandoned or forgotten?
- Do you feel you have lost someone?
- Have you lost contact with a best friend or family member?
- Have you lost or forgotten some of your most precious moments in life, e.g. fun, laughter, happy memories, birthdays, special occasions?
- Have you lost or misplaced some of your most treasured possessions, e.g. your home, special gifts, keepsakes or heirlooms?

How many times during your life did you feel you had lost something, and had then anxiously started looking for it, yet when you allowed your mind to slow down and relax, you could remember where you left it.

Supposing you think you have lost the keys to your car. Do you frantically run around the house, looking in the bathroom, under cushions, and turning out all your pockets, blaming everyone in the house for moving or taking them, and then suddenly remember that you left the keys in the car door?

How many times in your emotional life have you felt you have lost something, and do not know where to start looking for it? Family and friends may have lost their trust in you. You could have lost your trust in others, your belief in yourself, your courage to start again, your ability to carry on, your ability to change, your ability to live and be free, your ability to heal yourself, your ability to have a healthy relationship, your ability to have fun, or your ability to love.

One day you realise that you do not have those things anymore. Like the keys you left them out of your hands to do something else, and like the keys you do not know why, where, or when you have lost them.

In searching for reasons behind your losses, your tendency may be to blame. You may feel like blaming people in the caring profession when you lose a loved one, despite the fact they may have done everything in their power to help, support and care for your loved one. You may feel like blaming the educational system, when your child fails their exams, and loses the chance for higher or further education. You may blame family or friends for losing out on your childhood, and for not allowing you the joy and freedom of being a child.

It is often with the help of someone else that you can retrace your steps i.e. counsellor, therapist etc. You may be moving so fast that you cannot see what is happening in your life. You may be dashing back and forth between your GP, therapist and anyone else who will listen to you, as you search for what you feel you have lost in your life.

You may be taking medication in an attempt to suppress the pain you feel, as a result of this loss. You may have become attracted to temporary or unhealthy relationships or substances in your desire to fill the void.

All of this is only a temporary measure to keep you going until you find your original keys. These are only temporary means to keep you going, until you find the root cause of your losses.

- What caused you to lose your job?
- What caused you to lose your relationship?
- What caused you to lose your friends?
- What caused you to lose your most treasured moments or possessions?
- What caused you to lose your good health?
- What caused you to lose trust?

Sometimes it is only when we have lost everything, and we are at the bottom of the barrel and the only way is up, that we will take the time to look at ourselves and our way of life. Very often it is only when we desperately need something, that we seriously start looking for it.

Sometimes it is necessary to seek the help of professionals, so that you can look within yourself. Sometimes reading a book to which you are directed or discussing your dilemma with someone you can trust, can clarify what has been happening for you.

At some deep level you already know where and when you lost your friends, relationship, health or trust, also your most treasured possessions or moments, like having fun and laughter.

Affirmation:

Close your eyes, take a deep breath, exhale slowly and repeat to yourself:

Some things I have moved on from. Other things have moved on from me.

If I need to and if it is for my greater good, I can rediscover and find what I have lost.

I can learn what caused my losses.

I can get help to deal with and heal from my losses.

I can learn to treasure and take care of all the precious things in life that God has given me.

(61)
Trespassing

The garden in this story is about life, your life or anyone's life.

Are you trespassing – wandering in and out of another person's garden (life)?

This can be physical, emotional or mental wanderings.

Do you start off a sentence with "if?" "*If only, If she, If they, If he?*"

Do you deal with and try to resolve your own problems and issues, or do you concern yourself more with other people's problems and how they could resolve them?

- "If" they would only try harder.
- "If" they were different.
- "If" they would change their ways.

Does a lot of this problem solving go on in your head?

Do you do a lot of problem solving without taking any real physical action?

Look at a swing, – it goes over and back, over and back and nowhere.

Look at a yo-yo; – it goes up and down, up and down and nowhere.

Look at a pendulum, – it goes over and back, and round and round, until *you* tell it to stop.

If you yourself continued to walk over and back, and

round and round, in the same spot you would be going nowhere. Do you stop yourself? Does exhaustion stop you? Does ill health stop you, or do you wait until someone else tells you to stop?

Who tells your mind to stop?

- To stop wandering in and out of places that do not concern you.
- To stop wandering in and out of other people's lives.
- To stop wandering over and over old ground in your own life, but not really getting anywhere.

When a sentence starts with "If only"– the mind and body are living with regrets or hopelessness. You cannot live on an "if." "If" did not happen. You can learn from an event that has happened, but you cannot learn or deal with "if it happens."

Imagine every morning when you woke up, you went for a stroll in your neighbour's garden. You see all that he could do to improve his garden. You can see what his garden would be like; "if" he did all the things you think he should do. "If" he clipped his overgrown hedge, "if" he cleared out all his unnecessary rubbish. This garden is symbolic of the places your mind wanders to when it tries to resolve other people's issues in your head.

Do you have difficulty staying in your own space? Is your mind constantly thinking about other people, and wondering how they could solve their problems ("If only!")? You are exhausted going around and around *in your head.* (The trouble is you may not have got out of bed yet).

Does this happen to you in real life? Do you find yourself preoccupied with the problems of your family and friends? Do you find yourself constantly wandering in and out of their lives imagining all they could do to improve their lives (their garden), especially if they did all the things you think they should?

Your neighbour's garden is *his* life. You wander around thinking about him, and all the good things he could do with his garden (his life, his health, his relationships, etc). But the problem is, this is not your garden, and unless you are invited into your neighbour's garden (his life), you do not have a right to be there. You do not have a right to give your opinion on how he should plant his garden (on how he should live his life). Or, what type of shrubs he should have in his garden (what type of people he should have in his life).

It is your neighbour's own business;

- How he looks after his garden (his life).
- How well kept or neglected his garden is, (how well he looks after his health).
- What sort of fence he has surrounding his garden (what sort of boundaries he maintains in his life).
- How he nourishes his garden (how he nurtures and takes care of himself).

The only garden you are responsible for is your own garden. There may be no "ifs" in your garden, because the possibility is; you are not there either.

Now, what about *your* garden?

- When did you last look at your garden, (your life)?
- When did you last spend time in your garden?
- When did you last do some work on your garden (yourself)?
- What do you feel is the problem with your garden?
- Is it too much trouble for you to sort it out?
- Is it overgrown and out of control?
- What aspect of your garden (your life) do you have difficulty dealing with?
- Do you have painful issues in your life that you have difficulty dealing with?
- Does it seem like a momentous task to sort out your own

garden? Does this deter you from even attempting to clean up your garden (your life)?

- Is it the quality of your garden that bothers you (the quality of your life)?

Is it easier for you to focus on your neighbour's garden (your neighbour's problems; his family, friends, etc., and how he could improve them), especially if you cannot be held responsible, or be criticised for the condition of his garden?

You choose your garden (this life) this time around.

You can change and improve your garden (your life), but you can do neither of these things if you are constantly wandering into somebody else's garden (somebody else's life). You do not have the right to trespass and make judgements, suggestions or assumptions, about the way someone else's garden (life) should be, even if the wanderings are only going on in your head.

Your body does not know the difference between the thought and the action. After the hours you spend wandering (in your head) in and out of someone else's garden (life) you may be quite exhausted – going nowhere. It would be better for you if you physically went out and spent a day working on your own garden, (resolving your own issues and attending to your own physical, emotional and mental needs and well-being).

The next time you find yourself rambling into someone else's garden worrying, thinking and planning other people's lives (even in your head), say to yourself, "STOP!" "Is my garden so clean and well kept that I can waste time wandering into someone else's garden (life)?" "Can I afford to be worrying about someone else's garden (health)?"

Each time you feel you are starting to wander, say to yourself "STOP!" For a moment you may stop, but seconds later you may find your mind has started to wander again. If you say, "STOP" to your brain, the thoughts will stop momentarily, but you must learn to reinforce the word "STOP" over and over again. Do this until you reach a stage where the brain *will* "STOP." The brain recognises the practical reaction to the word "STOP!" i.e. a red light – DANGER STOP!

Once you have realised that you are spending so much time in your neighbour's garden, ask yourself, "Do you intend staying there?" Perhaps your time would be better spent cleaning up your own garden (your own health, your own life). In doing so your neighbour may get a good look at *his* garden. Did it ever occur to you that as you are trespassing on your neighbour's garden, someone else might be trespassing in your garden, making suggestions, criticisms and judgements about you?

Today do a little soul searching (garden searching).

To stop these wanderings you may need to continue practicing some "thought stopping exercises." As soon as your mind starts to wander say, "STOP!" Return to the present moment and what you are doing now. Practice some deep breathing exercises. When your mind starts to wander. Stop look around you, ask yourself, is your garden (your life, your health) in such good shape that you can leave it unattended?

When you are drifting from your garden, ask your guides to help you return to your garden (your own space). If you have already wandered away, it may be a valuable exercise to try and find out where, when, and why all this wandering began. What was happening for you that you left your garden in the first place? If the reason for your trespassing or wandering is difficult for you to resolve, you may need to seek professional help.

Affirmation:

I will stop wandering into other people's gardens.

I will stay in my own garden (my own space).

I will take stock of my garden (my life).

I will clean out my garden and restore it. (I will clear out old wounds and hurts and heal from them).

I will introduce new and exciting plants and flowers into my garden (new and exciting people and ideas into my life).

I will create a new garden for myself (a new life).

(62)
What You Don't Need

You don't need a digger to take out a thorn.
You don't need a holiday in the Bahamas to have fun.
You don't need a white bull to have a calf.
You don't need a house on the hill to keep the rain out.
You don't need a herd of cattle for one pound of meat.
You don't need a sledgehammer to drive a nail.
You don't need a generating power station to have light.
You don't need an orchestra to dance.
You don't need a choir to sing.

...Solomon.

(63)
Fear Of Letting Go

Do you have a fear of letting go?

Does someone you know have a fear of letting go?

Fear of letting go can control you and those around you.

Letting go allows you to move on to newer pastures. Letting go allows you to have new learnings and travel on new journeys. Letting go gives you freedom.

- Letting go of control, – allows others to have their freedom and their learnings.
- Letting go of conditioning, – allows for change.
- Letting go of relationships, – allows both people to move on with their respective lives.
- Letting go of a child when they have reached adulthood, – allows them to create their own learnings.
- Letting go of a job, – allows ourselves and others to move on.
- Letting go of goods, books, clothes etc., and dealing with your rubbish in an environmentally friendly manner, – helps to save the planet and stops waste and stagnation.

It is very easy for the conscious mind to say, "let go." You can tell someone there is no problem letting go, but it is like telling a man to *"let go"* when he is hanging from a cliff edge by his fingertips. Of course it is easy to *say* let go, but he knows the last time he let go in a similar situation, he broke his two legs. It does not matter how many people are there to catch him, – his subconscious mind may be continually telling him, – "It is not safe to let go."

Trying to talk someone through his or her fear of letting go, can sometimes be like hammering a wooden nail into a concrete floor. It will not go in very far. It is hard to penetrate the concrete (to break through the fear). This fear may have started in another lifetime, pre-birth, or in early childhood. Therapy may be necessary to decrease the intensity of the fear, also to identify the fear, and so allow the person to deal with it and move on with their lives.

What can you do?

- Identify your fear of letting go. Where it started, how it started, when it started.
- Feel your fear.
- Try not to allow your fear to control your life.
- Get help to confront and let go of your fears through therapy, counselling etc.

You are not alone in your fear.

Affirmation:

I give myself permission to let go of anyone or anything, that may be holding me or impeding me on my journey.

I will not allow fear of letting go to control me or attempt to control those around me.

(64)
Old Hurts

Would you like that someone would change his or her behaviour towards you?

This story may bring awareness to you that there may be "old hurts" which you may have covered up for years, old hurts that you may now need to deal with and heal from.

An event may have occurred early in your life, which may have caused you severe shock or trauma. Someone may now be triggering those old hurts. They may not be *causing* your hurt, but they may be *triggering* it.

There may have been times in your life, when you felt family, friends, or work colleagues were causing you undue hurt. You may have wished that they (the person) would change, but is there a possibility it is their *behaviour* you had wished would change, rather than the person?

This behaviour may be triggering deep physical, emotional and mental wounds from which you may not have fully recovered. For some, there is not just one incident of hurt, but many incidences reinforced over and over again over many years. Just because the scar is no longer visible, it does not necessarily mean that the hurt has healed. When we find ourselves in a situation where old hurts are being triggered we develop coping methods or "tools."

Each and every one of us develops coping methods, which help us survive in any given situation. These coping methods help to lessen the hurt or block it out altogether. The more severe the hurt or pain, the greater we will feel the need to block it. When old pain or hurt has been triggered, and we find ourselves unable to deal with it, we may behave or engage in unacceptable or inappropriate behaviour.

When you express how you feel to a person who is triggering your hurt, *you* may feel further hurt, because you do not feel heard. In explaining how the behaviour of those around you is affecting you, it is *important* to separate the person from the behaviour. Remember your partner, friends or family may also have old hurts either physical, emotional or mental that you do not see and may also be triggering.

You may be unconsciously triggering *their* old hurts or pain. *They* may use whatever "tools" or coping methods *they* can to protect themselves, or to block their pain or hurt from surfacing. For example, they may react to your "pain triggering" in an abusive or aggressive manner, or in a way which you may feel does not justify what you may have said or done.

You may have *triggered their* old pain or hurt, but you did not *cause* it. *You* are responsible for what you have said or what you have done, but you are not responsible for *their reaction* or how they may respond to you.

If you are allowing yourself to be a victim of their "tools of survival" i.e. their abuse, control or aggressive behaviour, then you must decide whether you want to remain in this situation or not.

Pain and hurt may have been suppressed since early childhood. When you feel hurt or let down by family or friends, it is important to explain to them, that it is their *behaviour* that you find unacceptable, not the *person* they are. To them their behaviour may be acceptable, so it is important for you to explain, that it is their *behaviour* that *is* causing you hurt, whether this behaviour is intentional or not.

A person who is trying to heal from past hurts may need a therapeutic environment, where they can feel safe enough, to uncover their wounds. These wounds may have been inflicted over many years and by many people.

Today, ask your God, your guides, your angels to help you, to remove those old bandages gently one at a time, so that you can uncover all those old wounds, hurts, pain, and heal from them. Remember, you may have been a child when you suppressed or blocked the hurt or pain, but you may now be an adult, an adult attempting to deal with those issues and trying to heal from them.

Affirmation:

I will learn to separate the person from the behaviour.

I will become more aware of any old hurts I may have.

I will get help to uncover these hurts and heal from them.

(65)
Confusing Messages

Confusing messages are saying one thing and acting out another.

Have you or someone you know been sending out confusing messages?

Do you feel people appear to be listening to you, but because of their reactions, you do not feel heard? Do you feel heard? Do you hear yourself?

Do you find yourself complaining to all and sundry about your health, your circumstances, your family and their behaviour but feel no one appears to be listening to you?

The questions you need to ask yourself are:

- Are you listening to you?
- Can you hear what you are saying?
- Do you believe yourself and what you say? If you do not believe or hear yourself, how can you expect others to believe you or hear you?
- Are your actions based on your feelings or on what you think you should feel?
- Are the actions and reactions of those around you based on what you say or on what you do?
- Can you say if the messages you are sending out, are clear or confusing?

Are you reliving some of the messages you received as a child? "If you are not sick, you are not entitled to be in bed." "If you are sitting down and there is work to be done, you are lazy." "If you are lazy, you are guilty of a sin."

Where and when did you first hear these messages?

At a very early age you may have discovered ways to help you survive. For example, if you wanted a day off school and you had no reasonable excuse, saying you were tired was not always good enough, but saying you felt sick nearly always worked. It was nearly always a guaranteed method of getting extra attention. You would get your favourite food and drink and you did not have to do your chores.

Your parents always gave you more attention when you were sick and nobody was allowed to argue with you or annoy you. Being sick certainly had its advantages but it had its disadvantages too. You had to be careful that you did not get better too quickly. If it was a sore foot, you could not start running around as soon as your brothers and sisters returned home from school. The disadvantage also was that you could not play any games, until your mum or dad decided you were well enough.

Unfortunately, over a period of time, we can lose the ability to state how we really feel. We sometimes go from the doctor to the therapist's clinic and to the hospital without any illness being diagnosed. Supposing someone somewhere did find a reason and a cure for that backache, would it really make you happy?

After all, that backache may have allowed you to avoid doing so many things you did not like doing for so long. This may be a real pain now but it is also a real survival weapon. It could have been your saving grace in so many difficult situations. Sometimes we feign illness and the body responds rapidly to our thoughts. For instance, in order to avoid issues or deal with problems, we may say we have a headache. The body can react by developing a headache.

As a mother, if you are tired and decide to lie down for a few hours and one of your children walks into the bedroom and asks, "mummy, why are you in bed?"– it is important to explain to them that you are in fact tired and need to rest.

As a parent you may have a tendency to use old weapons

and mislead those around you. Supposing lunch is not ready and the beds have not been dressed, you may feel guilty and have difficulty saying you are tired and have been busy doing other chores. You may now be more likely to resort to your old weapon saying, "I am not feeling well." This kind of answer can bring about fear and worry in a child's mind. They may think mummy is going to die, especially where they have a memory of a relative or friend, passing away after being ill.

Your husband arrives home sometime later and hears that you are not feeling well. Immediately upon hearing this he anxiously proceeds to cook the evening meal and offer you something to eat. He then makes sure the children do not make noise, fearing your condition may worsen. Now your survival weapon is working at its best – you get to rest, your children are given their dinner and then assisted with their homework, and you do not have to listen to them squabbling over toys or television.

On the other hand, if they ask what is wrong with you, and you truthfully – reply, "I've got a headache" or "I feel tired" then everybody is let off the hook because they know exactly what is the matter with you. You are not then seen as lazy, you do not feel guilty and your family understand that you get tired or get a headache at times and just need to lie down and rest for a while.

How do you behave in your relationship?

Do you send out confusing messages to your partner? Do you complain all week of a back problem, saying you are unable to work, mow the lawn or clean the windows etc., yet when the phone call came this evening inviting you for a game of squash, you instantly agreed?

Do you return from the game of squash still complaining, about the pain in your back, take a few painkillers and head off to a party?

Earlier in the week you complained of a sore throat, yet you spent a couple of hours standing in the pouring rain, watching your local team play football.

As a woman, you may say that your partner does not help you around the house. Did you actually ask him for help to move that wardrobe out of the back room? You did say it was too heavy, yet you somehow managed to move it yourself.

What messages are you sending out?

You may complain about not having adequate financial support, yet you somehow seem to manage to meet your commitments. You said you were not going to play any more tennis this year, at least not until you got your back pain sorted out, yet you spent several hours playing tennis one evening last week, and again had to take painkillers in order to get some sleep because of the pain.

What types of messages do you as a parent relay to your children? Do you tell your children that the pocket money you have given them must last them for a week, but when they request more money two days later, you give it to them without question?

You are sending out "CONFUSING MESSAGES."

You are saying one thing and acting out something else. As your children grow older you may loan them money and say, "I must have this money back by the end of the month, because the mortgage is due." They do not pay back this loan and say they do not have it, but they still go out partying all over the weekend, whilst you sit at home, worrying about where you are going to get money to pay the mortgage. This situation can go on in a family for years, with the parent / parents accepting it as an ongoing occurrence. The eventual amounts owed by the children can run into thousands of pounds.

Has there been a similar situation in the past, where you said you could not afford to pay for something for your children, but somehow, you still managed to do so? Do members of your family believe you anymore? When did you send out the first confusing messages to your children? Was it when they were babies? Did you say to them, "No you cannot have that lollipop or ice cream before dinner," but when they persevered you gave in?

As a parent you may take a child visiting a house where there is a dog. This dog may not be familiar with children, so the owner explains that it is better not to allow the child to go close to the dog. The parent turns to the child and says, "Do not go near the dog," but then begins to stroke the dog. (This child learned at an earlier age that this parent does not mean what they say). The child attempts to pat the dog, as he had seen the parent doing. The dog bites the child. The child is physically, emotionally and mentally scarred. It may be necessary to have the dog put down.

All of this has happened, because of this parent sending out confusing messages. Did your parents give you clear and concise messages, or confusing and unclear messages? Did they advise you that it was unsafe to walk home from the disco alone, but then did not arrive to collect you at the pre-arranged time? Did they encourage and sometimes insist on you exercising, playing sport and eating healthy foods, but they themselves continued to eat non-nutritional foods and did not exercise. As adults we may sometimes advise our children not to drink, smoke or engage in inappropriate behaviour, but yet we ourselves may do all of these things.

What sort of messages do you send out to your friends? Do you ask for help to do something, but then proceed to do it yourself, before anyone gets a chance to help you? You say you are tired, but act as if you have tons of energy. You say to your family that you did not sleep well last night, so you intend going to go to bed early tonight, but when your friends call, you sit up talking until late into the night.

If you are feeling unwell and decide to go to bed, then that is okay. Some hours later you may feel better and decide to get out of bed and go to town. Where younger children are concerned you need to bridge the gap between saying "I am unwell," and jumping out of bed and going to town. It is important to say, "I feel much better now, so I am going to get up out of bed and go into town." This in turn allows the child to learn that it is okay to lie down if you are feeling tired or unwell. It is also okay to carry on with your chores when you are feeling well again.

You may have been receiving and sending confusing messages for many years. Sometimes we can feel better within ourselves, when we feel we are fulfilling the wishes of others. Sometimes, it is not knowing our limitations that allows us to keep going, until we are burnt out and exhausted. Sometimes it is not having a strong sense of our own boundaries or limitations, that can allow us to change our minds at a moments notice.

Sometimes guilt can be playing a part in our actions or reactions. We may feel guilty if we take time out to rest without being sick. You may have experienced many years of confusing messages from your parents, teachers, and family. Did they make promises, only to break them over and over again? What were your role models like when it came to sending out messages? Did they send out confusing messages or were they clear and concise?

Can you recognise yourself in this story?

- Are you sending out confusing messages?
- Is your partner, friends and work colleagues confused by the things you say, and the things you do?
- Are your children confused by your behaviour?
- Are your children mirroring back to you and society, the confusing messages they have received or are still receiving?

What can you do to change your pattern of behaviour now?

You may need to look at your behaviour and the messages you are sending to yourself and those around you. Think back and reflect on your actions over the past hours, days, weeks and years. Think back and reflect on the actions and reactions of those around you, children, other family members, friends and work colleagues. Ask yourself if you can remember events that took place or could have been avoided, had you been sending out messages, which were more concise and clear.

Was there an incident or situation in the past, that you can remember, where you could have prevented an accident or situation developing, or worsening, had you relayed a clearer message? When you become aware of how your behaviour is affecting you and those around you, you have a choice as to when and how you can begin to change this behaviour.

Do not be afraid to seek help. You may need professional help to create clarity on how you may be relaying messages to yourself and those around you.

Affirmation:

I will say what I mean.

I will mean what I say.

I will send clear and concise messages to myself and those around me.

(66)
Negative and Positive

- If you leave a job or relationship because you do not want to be trapped – it is negative.
- If you leave a job or relationship because you want to be free – it is positive.
- If you try to score a goal to prevent you losing the game – it is negative.
- If you try to score a goal so you can win the game it is – positive.
- If you work hard so you will have enough money to survive – it is negative.
- If you work hard to have enough money to enjoy life – it is positive.
- If you sell your house because you are afraid you will not be able to meet your financial commitments – that is negative.
- If you sell your house because you can have something better – it is positive.
- If you move out of your space to see things from someone else's position – it is negative.
- If you stay in your space and observe someone else's perspective – it is positive.

...Solomon

(67)
Getting It Wrong

Are there days when you are full of confidence, outgoing, feeling good in yourself and you feel the world is your oyster?

Are there other days when nothing appears to go right for you and the harder you try the worse things seem to get?

Do you feel on those days that you somehow seem to be "getting it wrong" no matter what you do?

Do you feel you yourself are wrong because things do not work out the way you expected they should? Where did you first receive this message?

Understanding where the belief system may have come from sometimes can be of help. It is realising that you yourself are not wrong, when you do not come up to someone else's expectations of you. If you set goals for yourself that are unachievable, it does not mean you are wrong. It could mean however you may not know your own limitations. You could have picked up this belief system as a child. The messages and direction we receive as children set the pattern for a lifetime. The only person who can change that pattern, that belief system, – is you.

Take for example after a difficult labour and the previous loss of a six-month-old baby, a mother gives birth to a baby girl. The pregnancy had been monitored all along, but showed some complications at an early stage.

Following the birth, the baby required some minor surgery and was then placed in an incubator to recuperate. Because of the sudden isolation from her mother, the baby may feel a sense of rejection. This may be the little girl's first feeling of a sense of rejection, of not being right or not being acceptable.

This mother is very worried that her little girl is going to die. She is constantly asking what is wrong with her baby. "Is she going to be alright?" Even when the doctors try to allay her fears, the mother is still not convinced that her baby is all right.

The baby is eventually discharged from hospital with a clean bill of health, and makes really good progress. Her mother continues to worry about her. She is constantly checking her temperature, feeling her pulse, checking her breathing etc. With even the slightest change in the baby's condition, the mother exclaims to the father "there is something wrong with the baby," and calls the doctor. The words now echo in the baby's ears – "There is something wrong with her." As this little girl grows older she believes there really *is* something wrong with her.

Some people may say that this mother is neurotic, but each little sniffle from the child triggers the mother's own guilt, that she may not have acted swiftly enough, or in a responsible enough manner, so as to have prevented the loss of her first child.

The fear is stuck in the mother's energy field. The child in turn reacts to the mother's fear. When she hears that there is something wrong with her, the child does not fully understand what this means, but learns over the years that "wrong" is the opposite to "right." So if she constantly hears that there is something "wrong" with her, she may then interpret that she herself "is not right"... then it follows (she believes within herself) that she cannot do anything right.

Following on from this, the mother sees her child as delicate, and may not allow her to perform certain chores or tasks. The child in turn may interpret that she is not *able* to perform certain tasks, because she will not get it right.

As this girl grows older she may receive a good education and have all the appearances of being knowledgeable. She may be seen to have valid opinions on a variety of subjects, coupled with quotes and facts from books or television, but she may not have a belief in her own sense of self, or in the fact that what she says really matters to anyone.

She believes – "she cannot be right because there may be

something wrong with her." This lack of personal belief in herself, may also affect her looks, her weight, her temperament, her attitudes, her personality, and her abilities.

How can she possibly do anything right, when she herself is not "right," – or so she believes.

It is important to realise that even before birth, children can sense how we feel towards them. From the time they are born, our children will interpret and learn from how we ourselves cope in times of stress, fear or anxiety.

A belief system e.g. "I am wrong," "I cannot get it right," can be a belief system instilled in a child at a very early age, without the parents being consciously aware of it. It is important to speak factually to our children. When a child complains of being unwell, it is necessary to separate the illness from the person.

For example when the child says "I feel sick," instead of saying, "Well what is wrong with you?" you could say "Show me where you are feeling sick." "Where do you feel the pain?" or you could say "Show me where you are feeling the pain." There are many ways you could ask the question without suggesting that the child himself / herself is "wrong."

If you have experienced this type of belief system, be patient with yourself. You may need to look further than the belief system you have developed about yourself.

You may need help to retrace your steps, to where this belief system first began. It is understanding and accepting yourself that is important, not how others see or accept you.

- Know that you are not "wrong" when you do not come up to the expectations of others.
- If you are not successful in passing an exam, it may be because you had not acquired sufficient knowledge on the subject in question. (*You yourself* are not wrong).
- If you were unable to complete a task i.e. repair the broken lawnmower, it could mean your knowledge of the

task or subject was limited, rather than *you yourself being wrong*.

- If your children are continually becoming ill, it does not mean *you are wrong,* it could mean you have limited experience, where children and their illnesses are concerned. It could also mean that the illnesses they develop i.e. colds, flus and viruses, are out of your control.
- If you are constantly feeling that "you can never get it right" i.e. cooking, learning, coping or dealing with daily chores, it is important to separate you the person from the issues at hand – *You yourself are not wrong.*

Affirmation:

I am not wrong if I do not come up to the expectations of others.

I will not blame or criticise myself unnecessarily.

If I have limited knowledge, experience or abilities it does not mean that the person I am, is wrong.

(68)
Boundaries

Do you feel you have a problem with boundaries?

Do you feel other people have a problem with boundaries where you are concerned?

Boundaries are visible and invisible lines that we erect to create limits on ourselves, to prevent us going beyond a certain border or distance. We also create these boundaries, to prevent others crossing a certain limit into our territory. If you erect boundaries one day and remove them the next day, this can be very confusing for those around you. You may become very angry or annoyed when someone crosses your boundaries, but, if you do not create boundaries that are clear, concise, and strong, how can you expect others to recognise and respect them?

This story may or may not relate to you. It may help you to understand what happens, and the affects it can have, when the boundaries of a child have been broken.

When can the boundaries of a child be first demolished?

A child can have a relatively happy, normal, contented childhood. Then, somewhere in their lives, they may experience sexual, emotional or physical abuse. The child's mind being global, takes responsibility for all that happens around them. They look for direction from their peers, parents, teachers, religious leaders, neighbours and friends.

The child creates boundaries on what is right or wrong, by following the example of those around them. If the very people the child seeks guidance from, breaks these boundaries by abuse of any kind, what can this child use as guidelines in their own lives?

It is easy to see how a child can become confused.

Lets assume a friend of the family abuses this child. The child sees this person as a family friend, and does not understand how this person could do anything wrong or harmful to them. The parents, not knowing what is happening to the child, continue to have the perpetrator in their home, and treat him as part of the family. The child may believe that they themselves are wrong, and the perpetrator is right, because of this person being accepted within the family circle.

The child may believe that the parents will not believe them if they tell what is happening. The abuser, because of the shame and fear experienced by the child, can abuse and break boundaries with many children in the same family. The abuser can threaten physical violence, if the child tells anyone about what is happening. He can also bribe the child to remain silent, by showering them with money or gifts. He can threaten to abuse other children in the family, if the child does not adhere to his demands. What the child may not know, is that he is already abusing other family members, and is telling each child the same story.

The abuser can continue with this behaviour for many years. Once the child learns and realises that the behaviour of this so called friend is inappropriate and unacceptable, they may once again attempt to tell the parents or other persons, but shame, and fear of the possible consequences may once again prevent them from ever doing so.

The incident can create a feeling within the child of "being bad." The child may even believe that *they* caused this person to abuse them, and in some inexplicable way, may believe it was their (the child's) own fault.

The child can carry this burden throughout their entire life, and have difficulty creating or maintaining boundaries.

As they grow older they may not even question what someone in a peer position may request of them, even to where it involves pain and hurt at an extreme level, either physical, emotional, or sexual.

Later on in life they may suppress their right to have their needs met, or to ask for what is rightfully theirs, (after all, "bad people don't get good things," – or so they believe). This could be as simple as asking for time out to rest, or simply saying "no."

Asking for and receiving emotional, physical, or financial support might also prove difficult. The feelings of this person can become so suppressed, that they may feel "non existent" within themselves.

The personality of the abused person can be such that they may project a very "tough" exterior, but on the inside they may still feel frightened and vulnerable. It is very seldom that the victim will tell their story to family or friends, because at a deep level, they may still believe it is they who have done something wrong.

Always remember, the child is never wrong, the child is never guilty. The child is not responsible.

How does the abused person learn to cope?

They may learn coping abilities. They sometimes create situations where they experience rejection. This is because they reject themselves, and the only reality they know is a world of rejection.

Sometimes the adult may physically reject themselves by self-harming, becoming bulimic, anorexic, over-weight, underweight, or by neglecting their personal hygiene. They may try to suppress their emotional pain when it surfaces, by bingeing on food or other substances. This can be an attempt to 'push down' the pain or keep it at bay. The abused person may also turn to drink or drugs to further suppress pain. They may go through their daily lives always expecting rejection, and then when it arrives, it confirms in them (this adult who is working, through the mind of a child), that they must be a bad person, or they would not be rejected.

All of these coping methods can be applied to block the pain at a very deep subconscious level. From the time an incident such as abuse occurs, a person can feel they have lost their trust and their sense of identity. They may also experience feelings of pointlessness and depression.

They may sometimes isolate themselves from the company of people, where they might feel vulnerable and threatened. Sometimes they use tactics, which were used on them as children such as abusive or aggressive behaviour.

The child, who learned that the world was not a safe place, may actually strive to create a "super safe" place for themselves in later life i.e. by accumulating wealth, or becoming a recluse, or they may take up employment in the caring professions, where they may feel more safe and secure. They may have great difficulty trusting. They may involve themselves in numerous relationships, though never really trusting anyone completely.

In certain situations especially group situations, this person may try to make themselves invisible i.e. by not asking questions, by not asserting themselves, by sitting in an area where it is difficult for them to be seen. This can be so that the focus of attention is not directed towards them. They may feel if they are not seen, they are less likely to get hurt.

Therapy may be necessary to enable the abused person to deal with and heal from that which happened to them as a child. A child that needed to be heard. A child that needed to tell someone that something was wrong. A child that needed to believe that if something "bad" was happening to them, that they – the child, – had a right to be heard, and that the perpetrator could be stopped and punished.

If the child enjoyed playing sport and socialising etc. prior to the abuse taking place, they may stop all those activities from the time of the abuse. Life may have felt like it had stopped for that child because of what happened.

The adult now, may need to realise that they have not lost all those early capabilities – they just left them down – put them aside for a time. Sometimes that which was pushed to one side when we were eleven or twelve or younger, may need to be re-awakened gently. If your boundaries (your fences) were demolished at a young age, you need to erect them again – slowly – one at a time.

You may discover that your boundaries have been down for over forty years, and for eight of those years you have been in a relationship. If overnight you start to erect boundaries, your partner in this relationship, may feel that it is they who have done something wrong. It may be some incident that triggered a memory for you, of your boundary having been broken. Your partner may have no knowledge of what has happened in your past, and may not be aware that a certain incident triggered a memory for you. You can sometimes react strongly to a seemingly minor incident, because of fear. It can be a fear that whatever happened in the past, – is about to happen again.

Imagine if you and your partner built your house on five acres of land with no boundaries or fences, and you wake up one morning to find your partner has erected a twenty-foot high fence down the middle of the field. You would feel very rejected to say the least, especially if you did not know what you had done, or had not done to bring about this action.

If you are in a trusting, caring relationship, it may be of help to confide in your partner about what has happened to you as a child. You could also do this with the support of therapy. That is – if you feel it could be of help to you, to deal with and heal from your trauma.

You may have been a child when you suppressed the feelings of shame, hurt, guilt, anger or rejection, but you may now be an adult who is trying to deal with them and heal from them.

Boundaries in early childhood.

In early childhood, you may or may not have learned about boundaries. Assuming that you can take and use other people's possessions without their consent, is an infringement of their boundaries. Intruding at an inappropriate time, and consciously overstaying your welcome, is also a breaking of boundaries. You learn to knock and wait at a door until you are invited in. You learn to ask for what you want, – not just take it. You learn also how to create your own boundaries. You learn also how to recognise in what way and at what point, someone else may be crossing your boundaries. If one parent allows a child to overstep boundaries and the other parent does not, the child only learns confusion.

There are many different types of boundaries: Physical. Emotional, Mental and Sexual boundaries.

Physical Boundaries: (Our physical territory)

Imagine for a moment that you own ten acres of land and no sheep. Your neighbour owns one acre, and has twenty sheep. If you do not fence around your land, your neighbour's sheep (having no reason not to), will inevitably wander onto and graze on your land. This could continue for many years, until one day your awareness of the situation dawns on you. You decide to erect fences and stop this intrusion on to your land. Because so much time has passed before deciding to erect a boundary fence, you could find, that your decision might not be acceptable to your neighbour, and lead to all sorts of quarrels and difficulties.

We are all entitled to the privacy of our own space, room, home, etc. Someone might invade this space by entering without being invited. The boundaries of our bodies may also be broken, by physical or aggressive behaviour against our will. It is important however to erect your fences (your boundaries) as early as possible, and make them clear to those around you.

Emotional Boundaries:

How many times do you allow yourself to be emotionally abused and manipulated? How many times do you allow yourself to be hurt emotionally? How many times are emotional boundaries not distinguishable?

In your early childhood, one of the most important lessons you learn about is a boundary. If you were lucky enough to have parents who themselves had boundaries, their example would be of great benefit to you in later years. If the child sees a parent expressing anger, appropriate to the situation, they learn that this is acceptable. This shows an example of a reaction from a parent to a boundary being crossed, and allows the child to learn when it is safe to express its own anger. This in turn enables the child to have a healthy approach to boundaries in relation to their own, and other people's anger.

A lack of suitable parental mirroring, or reaction to a particular situation, may cause a child to become overwhelmed by their own anger and that of others, if there is no clear boundary for the child to identify. This also applies equally to all other emotional expressions i.e., sadness, fear, joy, love etc.

Sexual Boundaries:

It is important to learn about sexual boundaries as children. This can be by appropriate or inappropriate behaviours modelled by your parents. You learn about the right to privacy at a certain age. You learn that when the infringement or transgression of your privacy feels wrong, that you are entitled to object to it. You learn also to appreciate and respect the change in your boundaries as you progress through childhood and adolescence to adulthood. Boundaries learned in those early years will set standards for how you live your life.

Your boundaries can have messages, or different signals displayed on them. Some of these messages can be very confusing for you and those around you, especially if you erect very strong boundaries one day, and remove them the next day for no obvious reason.

What is the sign or message on *your* boundary?

"Broken boundary here."

"Anyone can cross here."

"Ignore anything I say or do."

Are you the person who says one thing, and acts out

something completely different? Do you send out confusing messages to those around you? Did you receive confusing messages yourself in childhood?

Open-ended boundaries:

Do you have a very high boundary fence in front of you with a sign clearly saying, "Do Not Cross Here," but when someone looks more closely at this fence they realise it is open at both ends (open-ended)? They can easily get around this fence (It is easy to get around you). Are you easily persuaded to do or say something, that you do not feel is right for you? Can this be as a result of guilt, or a fear of the consequences if you enforce your boundary? Do people pass no remarks on what you say, because they know if they persevere long enough, there are ways to get you to change your mind?

Weak boundaries:

Do you try so hard to maintain your boundaries, but when sufficient pressure is put on you, you succumb, collapse, or give in under strain? Do you find it difficult to stick with what you feel is right for you (to stand your ground), or do you give in for the sake of peace, even when it is detrimental to your health or well-being? As a child is it possible you felt your opinions did not matter? No matter how hard you tried to support or defend yourself, there was always someone stronger than you? Did you learn it was pointless to struggle or persevere with what you felt was right for you?

Flexible boundaries:

Do you persist with your boundaries for as long as you can, but then give in because "your arm can be twisted," depending on who is doing the twisting, and the circumstances at the time.

These fences / boundaries are erected to prevent some people crossing. Unfortunately it is not the people who respect you and your belief systems, who will use their power and strength of will to transgress your boundaries. These are not the people who will try to bend or break you. It is the people who have no respect for you, your way of being, your health or your life, who will attempt to make you bend to suit *their* needs.

When you allow your boundaries to be twisted and bent often enough, they are likely to break. This permitting of others to change your mind can come from a belief system that "*you don't matter*." (What *you* want or need does not matter, and that other people are more important than you and also their beliefs are more important than yours).

Invisible boundaries:

Are you yourself not sure exactly where your boundaries are? This can be very frustrating for you, and for those around you. These types of boundaries are difficult to define, and vanish and reappear at a moments notice. This can be a sense that you do have boundaries, but don't know when, where, why, and to whom these boundaries should be applied. This can be as a result of confusing messages from your role models i.e. parents, teachers, family etc.

Low boundaries:

Low boundaries can come from a low sense of self, insufficient depth or strength of will (a low sense of self-worth). Not a high enough sense of self, to enforce your belief systems.

The message you project may read, "Anyone who is able to or who likes to, can cross here." "I don't matter, what belongs to me doesn't matter, come and go as you please." This fence is just a guideline, (no real enforcement of boundaries here).

This can happen as a result of a child not being allowed to have boundaries at an early age. Sometimes the child will feel its boundaries are not respected. (He himself is not respected). So the feeling can ensue, "I don't matter."

Weak spots in this fence:

When someone knows your weak spots or "the buttons to press," they know they will get through to you, no matter how hurtful or painful it is for you. They know the weak spots in your defences.

What can you do about this?

Find your own weak spots. Find out how and when your resistance was weakened. Try to respond, rather than react when your buttons are being pressed.

We all have a need to be loved and liked. Lack of love can leave holes in your boundary fence. The lack of love in your life can affect you so much; it can weaken your defences. When someone is offering this love, by manipulative or hurtful means, the need to "fill in these holes, these vacant spots" by any means possible, even if it is harmful, hurtful, or damaging to your health, can be quite strong.

Unlimited boundaries, or no boundaries at all:

"The sky is the limit" as far as these boundaries are concerned. You will do or say or allow any event, with no reservations, and with no regard for the consequences for yourself or others. This can lead to very dysfunctional or addictive behaviour. This behaviour can be as a result of a childhood, where no boundaries were role modelled or enforced by those around you. You may need to retrace your steps and find out where this behaviour started. You may need to get some help to do this in the form of therapy, counselling etc.

Moveable boundaries:

(No concrete base. Belief system not very concrete).

You or anyone else depending on the mood or circumstance can move these boundaries. These boundaries can be very confusing because they can be transferred from one person to another, or one place to another without prior warning. People who move their boundaries to facilitate others can be called "people-pleasers."

"People–pleasers" have little or no regard for their own wants or needs. So long as the other person is happy, the people-pleaser feels happy also. What he doesn't realise, is that he cannot make anyone happy but himself. Happiness comes from within, not from without.

Strict boundaries:

Strict boundaries means your sign reads, "Warning do not cross these boundaries without my consent." "Keep your distance unless otherwise invited." With strict boundaries you will have learned about boundaries at a very early age. You will have learned about your limitations, and how to create limitations and boundaries where others are concerned. If you have strong and effective boundaries, thank those who encouraged, helped, and supported you in your learnings about boundaries.

Take time out today. Have a good look at your boundaries. See if they need to be repaired or replaced. You may need help to find out where and how, your boundaries were demolished in the first place. Learn that you have a right to your boundaries, and you have a right to enforce and maintain them where and when you need to.

Erecting new fences and boundaries may be a slow process. Your boundaries may get knocked down a number of times before you eventually manage to maintain them. But now that you are an adult, you can rebuild them, and reinforce them. As they get stronger, *you* get stronger. *You* can make the decision when to create them, demolish them, or change them.

If you create boundaries now, you create them within yourself, and knowing them within yourself, will enable you to respect the boundaries of others. You are now the adult, hearing the child within, responding, and acting, to the need to erect your boundaries again. You may need to seek professional help i.e. therapy, counselling etc.

Can you remember the last time you had a value on yourself, or a value on what belonged to you? Can you even remember what it was like to have boundaries? It felt good then, and it can feel good again.

Today, ask yourself; Have your boundaries been broken?

- Are you allowing your boundaries to be broken?

- What can you do now, to prevent your boundaries being broken in the future?

Affirmation:

I will learn to recognise when my boundaries are being broken.

I will give myself permission to say "no," when I feel my boundaries are being transgressed or broken.

(69)
The Train

Are you trying to understand where it all began?

Where did your life begin?

Where did the changes take place?

How, where and when did you act and react to the changes?

Could life have been more comfortable, more balanced, more harmonious for you? What have you learned from your journey? What are you learning from your journey? What do you want to learn from your journey? You do have choices. Whether you exercise your freedom of choice or not is your decision. Only you can decide.

You agreed to take a trip in order to experience and avail of more earth learnings. This journey was set up at a higher level (in Spirit) many years ago. If you can imagine when you entered this life it was like entering a train station. You had already decided where you intended to go, and which train you intended to board, in order to take you to a certain stage in your destination. You had also decided at what stage of your journey you would take over responsibility for driving your own train.

At an early age, it is possible you may have felt that you had very few choices. You may have started your journey, with a particular set of parents (first train) with their own individual belief systems, ideals and family circumstances.

You may have found that further along your journey you were changed to another set of parents (a new train) you may have been fostered or adopted by a family with completely different belief systems, and a different set of family values and circumstances.

You may have boarded a train that would travel along uninterrupted, without stopping or having any breakdowns until the end of your journey, (no major hassles, sicknesses or traumas in your life). Or, you may have boarded a train, in order to experience relationship problems, traumas, sickness, and challenges, but one, which would provide you with many learnings.

As you grew older, you may have began to realise that there were different rail tracks open to you, (different directions and different trains). You found that you could take a different route if you chose to. Sometimes these journeys were enjoyable and sometimes not.

You may have discovered as time passed by, that you were not happy with the conditions on a particular train, or the behaviour of its occupants (your family, friends, workmates). You may not have been happy either, with the behaviour of other fellow passengers (brothers and sisters). They impeded your progress by control, bullying, neglect and abuse. This family did not allow you the freedom to progress and develop your abilities. At times you may not have been able to see the doors or windows on the train that you had boarded (you could not see a way out, your vision was clouded).

You did however agree to take this particular train. As the journey progressed, you realised that you did not like the cold (indifference and rejection within your family). The food here was not so healthy either (there was nothing fulfilling for you here). No warmth in this family. As life continued, this journey became more uncomfortable (difficult relationships, unhappy work conditions, aches and pains).

In the early stages of your journey the responsibility for driving your train was taken over by your parents and teachers. You went wherever you were taken depending on *their* capabilities and sense of direction. This direction may not have always been in your best interest.

You are responsible for your own life.

As you grew older and had learned how to drive your own train, were there times when you unwittingly handed over the responsibility for driving your train to other drivers, drivers who were not necessarily qualified or capable of driving your train i.e. family members, relations, health-care practitioners, and friends?

As you learn more about life, you learn you are responsible for your own life. You are also responsible for the conditions you are prepared to endure. You can take back responsibility for yourself. (Drive your own train). You can make this train more comfortable for yourself. You can learn not to hand over responsibility for your (train) life to others.

What can you do at this point in time?

The journey of life can be long or short, comfortable or rocky, but you do have choices. You have the free will how, where, and when to make changes if you feel like it. You have the choice whether to get off this train or stay on it. You have the choice how, where, and when to get help in order to make the journey more comfortable for yourself.

You could jump off the train (leave that difficult marriage, job, or dysfunctional relationship). However doing this suddenly and without thinking or planning for the next journey would be like jumping off a moving train in the middle of nowhere. Jumping off the train may not be the answer. You could hurt yourself unnecessarily, and find it harder to get up and start all over again.

Conditioning tells us that we should not complain or ask questions. We are told to take what we get, that there are others much worse off than we are. However, if you stay on this particular train you may not survive. Maybe someone else could survive here and be quite satisfied with these conditions, but they may not be suitable for you, or your learnings. You may now feel quite worn out and battered from your journey. Some journeys are longer and harder than others (some learnings are more difficult than others).

You could check the alternatives you have, should you decide to stay on this train. You may need help and support to help you survive on this train or you may need help and direction as to how, where, and when it would be best for you to leave this train.

- There are many who can help, but they may not be on the particular train you are travelling on at the moment.
- You could check which station would be best for you to stop and descend at.
- Check what other routes there are available and more suited to your particular needs.
- Find which station offers the direction and support you need.
- There may be more people on this train and other trains, who are also dissatisfied with the conditions they are living in. When they see your courage in leaving this train (making changes in your life) to start a new journey, this may be the turning point for them to also consider leaving their unhealthy and unhappy situation.

Remember, everyone has a choice. Everyone has free will, whether they exercise this or not is their choice.

You do not have to stay where you do not feel it is safe or healthy for you, or where you feel there are no longer any learnings for you.

- Do not be afraid to look for help when the journey gets tough.
- Do not be afraid to clean up your carriage (clean up your health, your way of being and your behaviour patterns).
- This could allow others to see that *you* can make changes.
- Making these changes could bring you into contact with

other passengers and drivers whose company you may enjoy more.

- It could also bring you into contact with people who are prepared to share *your* journey in a caring and loving way.
- You can take responsibility for driving your own train. (Take care of, and take responsibility for your own life and your own health).

Affirmation:

I will not allow fear of change to hold me in a place where I am feeling unhealthy or unhappy.

I will see change as a challenge.

I know I cannot change anyone but myself.

(70)
The Subconscious Mind

Understanding how the mind works can be an aid to understanding the Self.

The subconscious mind holds both the negative and the positive memories. Painful and unhappy memories can be suppressed in the subconscious for a number of years. However, a trauma or an injury could be seen as being negative, but if we learn something from it, it then becomes positive.

What happens when a child experiences a severe shock or trauma? This shock or trauma can be physical, emotional or mental. In order to survive, the child must shut down on all levels, by suppressing the memory of the pain in the subconscious mind, until they feel equipped and strong enough to deal with it.

The physical level may be the cut or wound. We look at this cut or wound, feel the level of pain, clean it and stop the bleeding. By judging the pain level and watching how the wound heals, we know when it has fully healed. What we would not do, is put a plaster on this cut and leave it on for thirty or forty years. If we did our whole physical body would become infected.

The problem is that we do not see the mental or emotional body. Consequently pain is tucked away in the subconscious mind for many years. As it does not seem to be an emergency (like the physical bleeding) it can be suppressed or forgotten. Time passes on and sometimes the emotional and mental affects of the injury are never dealt with.

Take for example if a dog bites a one-year-old child. This child cannot cope with the shock and the trauma of the incident and so it shuts down on all levels physical, emotional and mental. The physical wound stops bleeding. It is cleansed and taken care of.

What happens in the subconscious mind?

The subconscious mind has stored a memory of pain and fear. There is now a fear in this child that if it allows itself to think about what happened, all the pain will return. The child that was bitten by the dog may now be an adult of fifty or sixty years of age. The physical wound may have long since healed, but every time this person sees a dog, they contract in fear. All the old fear from that first bite of a dog is triggered again. Logic (the conscious mind) says, "Look at this dog. He is not the same dog. He is old and feeble and completely fenced in." Seeing the dog triggers the memory in the subconscious mind, of the pain and trauma. This is what holds us, controls and stops us from moving on from the fear.

We can have many suppressed painful memories, traumas and fears. We may shut down on all levels physical, emotional and mental. We suppress the pain in order to heal. The memory of the pain may be triggered, but we can never again experience the exact same pain as we experienced initially.

Remember it was a child of a year old who shut down and suppressed the fear and the pain. No therapy can change what has happened. By working with the subconscious mind through therapy, the intensity of the fear can be decreased thus allowing the healing process to begin.

If you have old traumas buried in your subconscious mind you may need therapy to release those memories, deal with them and heal from them.

(71)
Lighting A Candle

You may have recently called on your God for help.

When you ask for help, it always arrives. It does not always arrive in the way you expect it.

Sometimes you may ask for help, but it may not be for your greater good that you receive what you request at this particular point in time.

You may ask God for help for a friend or family member. It may be some time later that you realise that your request was not for the greater good of this person at that particular time.

When asking for help it is important to be clear on what you are requesting. It is also important that you do not put any conditions on this request and that you accept the outcome as being for the greater good of all. If you are requesting help for another person, it is important to say at the end of your request, "Providing it is for the greater good of all." Whilst you may believe that what you are requesting is best for you or best for another person, it may not necessarily be part of the "grand plan," that either you or they receive this request at this particular time.

Although your guides hear and respond to your every call for help, it can sometimes add greater intensity to the request, if you simply light a candle and direct your thoughts through its flame. Using the energy of a lighted candle is also a very powerful means of sending healing light and unconditional love to anyone anywhere at any time. You can send healing energy to the earth, to all creatures, to the old or sick, or anyone who is going through trauma or upheaval in their lives. You can send inspirational energy to help someone applying for a job or studying for exams.

You can also use the power of a candle to help yourself to let go of someone who has passed into spirit. Sometimes it can be difficult to "let go" of someone you love. When they have moved into spirit, you can help them on their journey, by lighting a candle for them, sending them your love and wishing them well on their journey in spirit. You can light a candle and ask your higher power, God, guides, angels to help you to "let go of the connection that binds you," allowing both you and them to move on peacefully on your respective evolutionary journeys. It is not necessary to see this as "cutting the ties that bind," but rather as allowing both of you to have the freedom to continue on different paths whilst still connected to each other by unconditional love.

When you light a candle, you open the doorway to light. It is like a phone call to the higher beings for assistance. Lighting a candle is a physical action, and when coupled with a request, it connects you to "All That Is," the Universal Energies, Higher Consciousness, God. You must then "let go and trust" the outcome of your request. In letting go, you hand over your request and its outcome to the higher powers without preconditions. Given time everything, every action and reaction fits in with the greater universal plan.

(72)
Awareness

You reach a new level of awareness:

When you understand love and learn to love and respect everyone and everything around you.

When you see nature at work with all its awe-inspiring beauty.

When you see the world as one infinite mass of ever changing, interconnected energy of which you are an integral part.

When you accept and respect every human being, every bird, fish and animal in the whole spectrum of life.

When you appreciate the land, water, air, mineral and plant kingdom and realise how important a role they play in your world.

When you recognise and learn how to create harmony in your life, the environment and your world.

When you learn to "tune in" to and heal your own physical, emotional and spiritual bodies.

When you learn how to "tune in" with the flow of life and consciously connect with "All That Is" with unconditional love.

Today ask yourself: How aware am I?

Am I aware of my feelings and how I feel towards others?

Am I aware of my own state of well-being?

Awareness is working in the light.

Lack of awareness is working in the dark.

In a very simple example, let us assume that you cannot find the switch for a light in a room. If you are shown where the switch is, you are now *aware* of where the switch is. This is an *awareness*, which you did not have, prior to being shown where the switch was.

You may be unaware of how your behaviour may be affecting another person, persons or situation, but when you are made aware of how your behaviour may be affecting this person, persons or situation, you can never again deny your awareness.

You now must take full responsibility for your behaviour and the consequences of this behaviour.

Today ask your God, your guides, your angels:

To bring you awareness for whatever it is you need.

Show you direction where you may have gone astray.

Support you in times of need.

Lift you up when you are down.

Show you light where there is darkness.

Help you to recognise and become aware of the needs of others.

(73)
A Healer

Do you ever wonder if you have healing abilities?

The answer is yes.

Everyone has the ability to help themselves and others to heal.

You may be acting as a healer every day of your life and not be aware of it.

Someone asked me one day how they could be a healer. This question has been asked many times by people wanting to help. So I asked my guides, "What is a healer?"

They said we have all got the ability to heal ourselves, but we also have the ability to help others to heal themselves.

We would all like to be able to help others more. We may feel that to heal we must be doing something major like healing a major illness, discovering a new healing remedy, or resolving somebody's emotional problems.

We live in a material based physical world of fast cars, fast living and highly advanced technology. It is a world of gadgets and quick fixes. Gadgets which remove much needed exercise and learnings from everyday life. We have medicines for quick fixes rather than taking the time to find the cause so as not to make demands on our time. A world of action rather than feeling.

What about the art of conversation, or the art of listening?

- Do we take the time to really listen?
- How many times do we listen without hearing?
- Do we give solutions without hearing the precise ques-

tion?

- Do we answer before the question is complete?
- Do we give back the power to a person to heal themselves, or do we try to take over their healing process?

The guides say, observe how you react the next time you are walking along the road and you meet your neighbour. Do you say, "Good morning, how are you," but then walk quickly past them, in case they stop and start telling you how they really feel?

- Do you ask them how they are and then tell them they are looking great, all in the same breath?
- Do you cross the road to avoid them in case they keep talking for ten minutes, delaying you and keeping you late for your appointment?
- Do you walk straight past them, pretending you did not see them at all?

If you want to be a healer, you could start by saying, "Good morning," ask them how they are. They may reply that they have been out of work all week because of the flu. If you can offer some suggestion that may help, then do so, but there is no need to go into a long tirade about *yourself* and all belonging to *you* and all that happened to *you* last week and how *you* dealt with the flu.

All you have to do is *listen for a moment* and perhaps make a few suggestions.

It is up to them whether to heed you or not.

It is that simple.

Now you have become a healer.

Another example is, if someone has a problem with their child, partner, spouse or family member and you spend even one minute really listening, then you are giving that person the space to heal. Now you are helping someone to heal. As a healer you do not need to take responsibility for someone else, but rather give him or her the power to heal themselves.

Imagine you have a bucket of water and you share this with your neighbour when he is thirsty. In relieving their thirst you are now helping them to heal. But you can also tell them where the well is, and in showing them where to find water, you are helping them to heal themselves.

Passing on information that may be helpful to someone is empowering him or her and is also a form of healing. You can help someone to heal by empathising with them, by sharing some of your experiences, and how you dealt with them, which may be similar to theirs. This may allow them to feel less alone and give them the courage to seek further help if necessary.

Today, be a healer.

Do one small task to help a neighbour or a friend.

(74)
Ripples

A thought is like a pebble in a pond – once you drop the pebble in the pond, the ripples begin.

It may take a long time for them to spread out and reach their destination, but they will eventually reach the edges of a shoreline and return back to you.

Every time we move we change the energy around us.

Every time we have a thought, we begin to create a new reality.

Be careful of stones that you throw. They may come back to you some day, sometimes when you least expect them.

When two people become involved in an argument, they are directing a particular vibration towards each other. One or other may be feeling a sense of injustice at something the other person has said or done. If either person is feeling a sense of injustice, the emotion associated with this feeling can be one of anger. If the person feeling the anger does not express it, and deal with it, appropriate to the situation, the reason for the anger cannot be resolved.

We all have the choice as to how we deal with our feelings and emotions. Past coping methods may sometimes be applied in an inappropriate manner.

By dealing with issues at the time they happen, you can prevent suppressed and unresolved feelings and emotions from becoming a part of a future argument or dispute, where they are not relevant.

When you are expressing an emotion such as anger, you need to be aware of what proportion of this anger is relevant to the present issue, and that the intensity of the anger that you are directing towards a particular person is justifiable. Could the intensity of this anger be as a result of many years of unresolved and suppressed angers? It could be a case of "the straw that broke the camel's back," with regard to the person who may be on the receiving end of this intense anger? This person knowing they are not responsible for the intensity of the outburst may not be prepared to take the full force of your anger on board. They may mirror back the full force of your anger to you, and you may not like it.

Do you blame this person for mirroring back your anger, or do you take responsibility for your own anger and the intensity of it? When you send out vibrations such as anger, hate, resentment etc., given time, they will return back to you (just like the ripples on the shore), in order for you to deal with them.

Do you continue to feel angry even when the other person acknowledges the part they played in triggering your anger? Is it possible this anger is still with you, because someone challenged your point of view? Did you personalise their reaction and feel threatened, or put down when this happened?

You may still be vibrating at an angry frequency long after the event has passed. This could be because even though the other person appeared to listen to your side of the dispute, you may not feel heard, judging by the way they reacted to you. This can increase your anger and frustration even more.

You may still feel angry because even though the other person listened and heard your point of view, they may not have agreed with you or your point of view in the midst of a heated argument or emotional or physical outburst.

Someone that sends out a peaceful and calm vibration can arrive on the scene of an argument or angry outburst. This calm vibration can diffuse or decrease the intensity of what is happening. This type of vibration can be likened to pouring cold water on a raging fire. It does not mean that the reason for the dispute or argument has been resolved. It means the intensity of the feeling between the two people has been decreased or diffused, thus allowing a possible reconciliation in a peaceful and harmonious way. A calmer slower vibration has the ability to change the atmosphere and vibration between numerous people. They can do this by remaining calm and slowing down the higher, more angered vibrations (vibes) being set up between the people who are arguing.

You can choose to express your feelings in a manner that is neither harmful, aggressive, judgemental nor blaming. You can choose to deal with your feelings as they happen. This creates a vibration of "going with the flow." There is no build-up of anger here. You can choose how you relate to another person. You can relate to them at the same frequency that they are sending out, or you can stay in your own space and vibrate at your own frequency.

You can leave your space (your own vibration), and try to get into someone else's vibration by trying to tune into their frequency and by then telling them what *you think* they want to hear. They know you are being unreal, and can react in a dismissive or angry manner. This person may have picked up on the vibration that you were sending out i.e. minimising, maximising or placating. You in turn can reflect back an angry or confused vibration, because your over exuberant vibration was not reciprocated as you expected.

You must take responsibility for leaving your own vibration in the first instance. If you are not sending out a real and truthful vibration, you cannot expect to get a real and truthful vibration returned back to you.

The next time you find yourself either in the company of people who are engaging in arguments, angry outbursts, or disagreements, especially if it does not concern you, try and stay in your own space, your own vibration. Observe what is happening around you. Feel your own feelings in the midst of the storm.

You may feel calm within yourself because arguments or quarrels may not be triggering a fearful emotion for you. Try and not get caught up in the vibration of others, i.e. if for you there is fear associated with arguments, you may experience a feeling of fear. Try not to allow the fearful vibration to control you. Feel your fear and then decide what action you wish to take.

If someone is reacting in an angry manner as a result of something you have said or done, you need to take responsibility for your own behaviour. If you try to deflect their anger by blaming, justifying, minimising, or excusing what you have said or done, you will only create a more intense angry vibration. This person will continue to mirror back to you, the consequences of your behaviour, until you take responsibility for that behaviour and deal with it.

It is important not to confuse mirroring back someone's anger with not taking responsibility for your own behaviour. For instance supposing you forget to deliver an important message. Because of this the other person may become quite angry, – which they are entitled to be.

Do you react angrily saying;

"You asked me to do too many things at the same time, and anyway you did not do what I asked you to do last week?" – (This is transference).

"It's no big deal, can't I do it tomorrow?" – (You are now minimising).

"Why didn't you get someone else to do it if it's that important, obviously I can't be trusted?" – (This is avoidance).

"You mustn't have made it clear to me, what it is you wanted me to do, otherwise I would have done it." – (Now, you are also blaming the other person and insinuating the reason you didn't deliver the message was because of the *way* you were asked to do so).

"I'm doing the best I can, I know you are working very hard too." (Now you are placating).

"Why don't we go out for a drink this evening, you need a break, you're in bad form all day, are you not feeling well?" (Now you are distracting).

At this point the other person may be starting to get really annoyed and frustrated. This is not just because of what you have done or not done but also because of your inability to admit the truth and your lack of acknowledgement of your behaviour. The consequences of your behaviour may also be causing further anger and annoyance for the other person.

Do you now say, "You did not say you wanted it delivered today?" This is despite the fact you heard the other person asking you to deliver the message today. This is attempting to put the blame for your behaviour back on the other person.

Because of the way you answered and the manner in which you reacted when asked to deliver the message, the other person is convinced that you clearly heard what it was they asked you to do. This person may become more and more angry and may persist in trying to make you acknowledge and take responsibility for your behaviour.

The situation may now be getting out of control. You may begin to feel cornered and feel a need to defend yourself. You may make another attempt to back track and diffuse the situation by saying, "I didn't hear you saying it." This again is despite the fact that you *did* hear the request. You are in denial and the other person is now furious and is in a state of high tension, rage and anger.

The vibration between you and this person is rage, anger, injustice and fear. Do you then try to diffuse the situation further before it reaches breaking point, or do you allow it to continue until you or the other person screams, breaks down, breaks something or falls apart completely?

Do you then decide to back track to where it originally began and try to explain and justify your behaviour? What you have done now, is you have taken the justifiable angry vibration and turned it to your advantage. The other person is broken now. They will accept any excuse for your behaviour. But what you must remember is that the angry vibration is still there. The reason for it in the first instance has not been totally resolved and will be reflected back to you again and again until you take full responsibility for all of your behaviour and then deal with it.

In order for you to change your behaviour, you may need to look at the possible reasons behind this behaviour. You may need to ask yourself what it was that prevented you from telling the truth in the first instance.

- Was it fear of the others person's possible reaction if you admitted the truth of what you had or had not done?
- Was it fear of the criticism you may receive as a result of what you had or had not done?
- Was it guilt and shame that stopped you admitting the truth when you realised the consequences of your behaviour?
- Is lying a habit you have developed over many years?
- Is denial an automatic response to situations you do not want to deal with or do not feel capable of dealing with?
- Is your reality rows and arguments? If this is so you may need to ask yourself, are you recreating this reality whenever an opportunity arises for you to do so.
- Is it a power struggle for you, to see another person broken and humiliated?
- Is there a need within you to control what is happening around you?
- Do you play mind games with other people?

The next time you find yourself in a similar situation, ask yourself; are any of the above questions relevant to you or your behaviour?

In being truthful i.e. by saying; "I am really sorry, I completely forgot to deliver your message," you allow the other person the space to feel and express their anger and annoyance. You also allow the space for you both to learn and deal with what has happened in a healthy and appropriate manner.

There are many ways you can respond to someone else's angry outbursts.

Imagine you arrive late for an appointment. When you arrive at the person's door they tell you how really annoyed they are.

Do you (A) exclaim, "The traffic was dreadful?" "I was late starting off." "I tried to phone, your line must have been engaged." (Incorrect behaviour – these are just excuses, justifying your behaviour, increasing angry vibrations from the other person).

Or (B) do you say as the person opens the door, "Hi, isn't it a lovely day, spring is here at last." "You're looking great." "How are you keeping?" (Incorrect behaviour – sidetracking the issue, – this behaviour is not allowing the other person the space to deal with their anger and annoyance).

Or (C) when the person opens the door and tells you that you are late for your appointment, do you reply, "Who are you to complain, you have been late for the last three meetings which we had arranged?" (Incorrect way of dealing with the issue, – this is direct confrontational behaviour).

Or (D) do you say, "I am really sorry for being late. I will make another appointment to see you at a later date, if it is not convenient for you to see me now." "I quite understand why you are angry and annoyed?"

You have now acknowledged the other person's anger and annoyance. You have given them the space to express and feel their anger or annoyance. You have not ignored or increased the angry vibration. You went with the flow of the other person's anger, without blocking it, minimising it, or denying it. This situation has now been diffused and dealt with, because of your acknowledgement of the part you played in triggering this person's anger.

The amount of anger this person is feeling may not be totally related to you. You only need to take on board and resolve within yourself and with the other person, the part that *you* are responsible for. You have now changed the vibration (vibes) around the incident.

What you have sent out now is what will come back to you, – good vibrations (good vibes).

The next time, *think* before you engage in a dishonest act or deed. – You may have to deal with the inevitable backlash sooner than you think.

Think before you engage in a verbal or physical outburst of anger or rage.

T*hink* about what you are doing or why you are doing it.

How would you feel if the ripples you are sending out, are returned back to you again some day?

...Solomon

(75)
Distractions

What are distractions?

Distractions; are any act, deed, or substance that may be used by ourselves or others, to avoid, minimise, suppress or keep physical, emotional or mental pain at bay. They can also be used to keep the feelings associated and related to the particular incident or trauma suppressed or at bay.

Were distractions used on you as a child? When you fell over and bumped your head were you held, soothed, and comforted until you stopped crying, or, were you picked up quickly, your tears wiped away, and you were then given something to play with? Or. Were you picked up and then taken to look out the window and told, "Look at the birdies," "Look at the moo cows?" This may distract you from your pain for a few minutes. You can't see any birdies or moo cows, and your head still hurts, – so you start to cry again.

Were you sometimes told, "Don't be crying it's only a little bang." – "You're a big boy/girl now, big boys or big girls don't cry over little things like that." – "I'll get you a nice biscuit, and then you will feel much better?"

Eventually after a half a packet of biscuits and a few lumps of chocolate, you don't need any more distractions. You have forgotten your sore head for the time being. You are covered in biscuits and chocolate, inside and outside. You now have a tummy ache and start to cry again. This time you may get a painkilling remedy in order to quieten you down and stop you crying. If that doesn't work, someone may have to come up with more effective distractions, which will take your mind off your pain, i.e. take you for a walk, or bring you for a spin in the car etc.

Can you see how distractions for an adult could have started very early in childhood?

- The first message we may receive is, – *"Ignore the pain."* (Pretend it's not there and it will go away).
- If it doesn't go away, – *"Minimise it."* (It's not that bad).
- If it persists, – *"Block it in any way you can."* (Stop it by whatever means possible).
- If it continues to surface on and off, – *"Find another more powerful distraction."* (A more powerful means of blocking the pain).

As you grew older, and someone did or said something to hurt or upset you, which made you cry, – were you encouraged to sit down and talk about it? Were you asked, "What exactly happened, how did it happen, where are you hurt, where do you feel the pain, what did this person say or do to upset you?" Or, were you told, "It's not worth crying over?" "They didn't really mean it." "I'll bring you into town later and buy you something nice for yourself."

This may be a distraction, to take your mind off your pain or hurt, – but it has not resolved it. The pain or hurt has been dismissed, minimised, and pushed to one side. It has not been dealt with in an appropriate and healing manner.

Later in life did you discover distractions that worked for you, i.e. when you felt tired and upset, did you reach for the biscuit tin or chocolate bar, or the cup of tea or coffee, or other stimulant? Or, did you honour your feelings and talk about why you were upset, and then treat yourself to something nice and rewarding for having the courage to deal with what was upsetting you? If you were feeling tired, did you lie down and rest or did you use stimulants to keep you going and then make numerous phone calls, to take your mind off your tiredness?

As an adult do you still use distractions from time to time?

- Do you use distractions when feelings surface that you

are not ready, or able to deal with?

- Do you have a fear of feelings?
- These can be feelings of hurt, pain, loneliness, loss, sadness, anger, guilt, grief, remorse, shame, low self-esteem, anxiety, anger or fear.
- Do you or have you used distractions such as incessant or persistent phone calls to family or friends, continuous cups of tea or coffee, bingeing on food, sweets or alcohol. Are you constantly watching TV, listening to the radio, exercising, socialising, cleaning and scrubbing, even when it is not necessary? Are you continually calling on neighbours and friends for a chat, or making numerous unnecessary trips to the shops or to town?
- Do you engage in a lot of these behaviours without really enjoying them, and sometimes not even notice or question the reasons, why you do what it is you do or say?

Next time *before* you use distractions ask yourself:

What is happening for you at this moment in time, i.e. are you sad, lonely, fearful etc? What are you feeling? You need to identify the feeling. Know it is safe to have feelings. Feel the feeling. Claim the feeling. Honour the feeling. This feeling is yours, and yours alone.

Whatever happened to create this feeling can never happen again. The fear of the feeling is sometimes greater than the actual feeling itself. The fear can be that if you get in touch with the feeling, and allow yourself to feel the feeling, you will be unable to cope. You will be unable to survive. You will fall apart.

What you need to realise is, you have already lived through and survived what is causing the feeling. You can never again experience the trauma, incident, or accident that caused these feelings, even if you wanted to. How do you know if something is better or worse, if you do not allow yourself to feel? If you do not feel you cannot heal.

You may have learned to block painful memories as a child. *You may have learned that it is not safe to have feelings.* You may have learned to associate feelings, with hurt and pain, never having learned to associate feelings, with love, joy, and happiness.

You may use distractions to avoid or block unhappy or painful memories, but it does not mean the memories have gone away or disappeared. When you reach for a distraction, rather than allow yourself to feel the feeling those memories can be triggered again and again either by someone or by a particular event until they are dealt with.

- When you reach for a distraction rather than allow the painful memory of the loss of a loved one, you are not dealing with the feeling.
- When you reach for a distraction rather than deal with hurtful remarks or deeds inflicted by another, you are not dealing with these issues or feelings.
- When you reach for distractions to suppress memories of hurt, shame, guilt or remorse, you are not allowing yourself to heal from these issues and deal with the feelings.
- When you use distractions rather than deal with the anxiety and fear around what somebody has said or done, or what they are likely to say or do, you are not dealing with the feelings related to the incident or possible incidents, – you are pushing your feelings to one side.

Try and identify the feeling, i.e. anxiety, fear etc., around what has happened (or what you fear is likely to happen), based on past experiences.

FEEL THE FEELING.

You have a right to your feelings. Your feelings are as a result of something that has happened to you, – a trauma, incident or accident.

The next time when you think about doing something, especially something that is not really important at this point in time, take a deep breath and ask yourself:

- Why am I doing this?
- Is what I am doing really necessary at this point in time?
- Am I doing this because it is a challenge, and I really enjoy it?
- Am I doing this to improve my health and general well-being?
- Or, am I using this substance or engaging in this behaviour as a distraction, in order to avoid some painful feelings and keep some painful memories from surfacing?

The next time before you reach for that bar of chocolate, cup of tea or coffee, ask yourself: Are you really hungry? Are you bored? Or. Are you trying to keep some painful memories at bay?

The next time you feel like bingeing on food or drink, ask yourself:

- Are you really hungry, or are you trying to suppress some painful memories?

The next time before you reach for that cigarette, drink or addictive substance, – ask yourself:

- What is going on for you?
- What are you feeling?
- Are you afraid to relax?
- Is there a fear that if you relax all your old painful memories of loss, hurt, pain etc., will surface, and you won't be able to deal with them or suppress them again?
- Before you reach for the telephone, ask yourself, what are you feeling? Are you feeling lonely? What is the reason for your loneliness? Have you had a recent loss or

bereavement, which you may need to deal with and heal from?

- Before you reach for your distraction, try and get in touch with what you are feeling first. Deal with your feeling. Try and find out what is causing the feeling. Once you have felt the feeling and dealt with it, you can never experience that particular feeling again. Doing this will allow you to move on with your life.

Suppressing emotions is like keeping a balloon pushed down in a bath of water. But once you take your hand off, it rises up again. The effort spent in suppressing and avoiding emotions can cause exhaustion and ill-health. You may find as you learn to deal with your feelings and emotions, as and when they happen, you will have less and less need or reasons for distractions.

Relaxing by choice rather than using unhealthy means to force the body to relax, can be healing for body, mind and spirit. Getting in touch with the feeling before stuffing the body with unhealthy food substances may help the person to lose weight, or gain weight if necessary.

Using distractions is not a solution to a problem. It may keep the problem at bay initially, but long term in order for you to heal, you need to learn to deal with your feelings how and when they occur.

In order to get in touch with your feelings, you may need to sit down and quieten the mind.

Lighting a candle and listening to relaxing music can sometimes help to allow you to focus on the particular issue, incident or trauma which you may have a fear of feeling, or difficulty dealing with. As you concentrate and focus on your particular issue or trauma, allow the memory of what has happened to come to the fore. You may find your eyes welling up with tears as your body begins to “feel” once again the emotions relating to that particular event. (All the time remembering, whatever has caused you hurt or pain can never happen again).

- Allow yourself the feelings. Feel the feelings, claim the feelings, honour the feelings. They are yours and yours alone. They are your response to a particular incident or trauma in your life.
- Allow the tears to flow.
- Allow yourself to cry. Cry, cry, cry, cry, cry.
- Allow yourself to feel the feeling throughout your entire body.

This is the beginning of your healing process.

You may also feel as you are going through this process, that you have a need to express or verbalise your feelings to someone. It may not be convenient or appropriate for you to do this at this point in time, but giving yourself permission to do so when it is convenient, gives you the freedom to move on and heal. It may be something you had suppressed, avoided saying, or felt you couldn't say at the time of the incident.

Depending on the severity or intensity of your trauma, you may feel more safe and secure in dealing with your feelings, in a therapeutic environment, i.e. with a professional therapist. However, you may feel safe and secure in the company of someone you love or trust. Whatever you feel is right for you, – that is okay. The feelings that may surface can be anything from grief to fear, to anger, to loss etc.

Allowing yourself to "feel," "own," and "express" your feelings can help clarify what is happening for you. It can allow you to heal, and also create closure on the trauma or incident. What was once used as a distraction, can now be a challenge i.e. sorting out your garden can be a creative and enjoyable experience, rather than a distraction.

Making that phone call can allow you to make connection, exchange views and opinions with friends and loved ones. It can also allow you to share some fun and laughter in the comfort of your own home. Having and sharing a cup of tea or coffee, or a drink with a neighbour or friend can enable you to exchange some new ideas and have some fun.

Affirmation:

Today I will look at where, when and what I may be using as distractions in my life.

As I learn to deal with my feelings. I will not need distractions.

I will learn to love and enjoy what I am doing, rather than using unhealthy or addictive substances or behaviours, or my time or money as a source or means of distraction.

I will not use distractions to avoid dealing with my hurt or pain.

I will become more aware of when and where, how and why, I may be using distractions.

When I have allowed myself to feel my feelings, claim my feelings, honour my feelings; I will reward myself for having the courage to have done so.

(76)
Right And Wrong

What is right? And what is wrong?

It is only our own perception which distinguishes which is right or which is wrong.

If you see a tree on the shore of a lake, at a certain angle you can see a reflection of the tree in the water, which looks upside down – or is it?

Now if you stand on your head and look again, the tree in the water appears the right way up but now you are upside down.

If you see a tree growing on the side of a mountain, the tree will look off balance as if it is growing at an angle. But if you tilt at an angle, the tree will look straight. However, now you are off balance – or are you really?

Which is right and which is wrong? – Neither.

...Solomon.

(77)
Karma

"Karma" can otherwise be called "Cause and Effect."

Cause and effect is in operation throughout the universe. In other words every action creates a reaction. Everything you have said or done in the past is affecting you now, and what you do, say or think now, is shaping your future. When you pass once again into spirit you are given an opportunity to "look back" on your past life. You can then determine what you may have learned from that particular life and what you may still need to learn. You will see how you lived your life and once again see the affect your deeds and actions (good and bad) have had on others and yourself.

If you so choose, your next earth life will include learnings, which you may need for your expanding awareness and evolvement. You can determine what sort of earth-life you would like to experience that would best fulfil your needs.

In order to advance on our ultimate spiritual journey, we must know and understand the implications of our actions. Each of our acts has two direct effects or results (one that is immediate and one that is delayed); there are also wider repercussions or secondary effects. For example, take someone who in a moment of anger, breaks his neighbour's window with his fist, and cuts his hand while doing so. The cutting of his hand is the immediate consequence, while the damages he must pay his neighbour constitute the delayed results. (If he does not make recompense, he will be forced to do so at some later time) The affects of his actions on others constitute the repercussions or secondary consequences.

The same law of the universe applies equally to our good actions. A good deed or action will in turn bring about "good luck," and good reactions. We need to be aware of the consequences of any wrongdoings towards our fellow men, because if we do not repay and redeem them in this life then it will be registered in the universal energy field, and karmic repercussions will inevitably balance the debt eventually one way or the other.

Each being or spirit has its own individual path to travel. This is their free choice, chosen "in spirit" before they reincarnate and are reborn as a person here on earth. They must then deal with worldly conditions, laws, governments, the environment, relationships, stresses and pressures, plus many other factors that can impose restrictions on the full expression of their free will. The challenges they take on when they reincarnate, are to express themselves fully "who they are," and "who they want to be," within the confines of a physical existence.

There is no such a thing as a fixed number of incarnations. This is up to the individuals themselves. You might be or you might meet a person who has returned to settle a karmic debt incurred by a wrongdoing in a previous life. Such a debt can be worked off in one crucial moment, or over six years of life, or it may take a lifetime or even more, in which case you will have to return to "balance the books" in yet another lifetime. This is karma at work.

There may be times you feel the "burden of life," is too much to bear, when you are paying off a past debt for ill-will, mis-deeds, or past transgressions. If on the other hand you are one of those "lucky" people who seem to be able to do no wrong, or are always in the right place at the right time, you are probably reaping the rewards and benefits from past good deeds, either earlier in your present life or from past lives. From this, you may come to the conclusion that there really is no such a thing as luck, but only hidden design and karma.

In choosing your parents and their genetic factor, you were aware of the possible physical, mental, and emotional attributes you could acquire. We sometimes choose parents for what we see as negative aspects rather than their positive aspects. There is little point in choosing parents who are millionaires if we want to learn about poverty, that is, if they remain millionaires throughout their lives and we reap the benefits of their wealth. There is little point in choosing parents who will remain poverty stricken, if we need to learn about wealth, or if we need to learn about the abuse of wealth and power. There is little point in choosing a home and family for a lifetime of disharmony if we want to learn about peace and harmony and visa versa. There is little point in choosing a family where there is ongoing loss, grief, sadness and hurt, and very little experiences of happiness and joy, if we want to learn about joy, happiness and laughter.

The learning we choose can be long or short, but once we have experienced our initial learning (the reason we returned for an earth experience), we may choose to move on and experience many more learnings of different types, different lengths and from many varied, interesting, and exciting sources. Having been born, you are still free to choose the finer details of your experience, to make the best or worst of your life, to fulfil it or let it drift aimlessly, or even to embark on a career of cruelty, selfishness and destruction.

You are making that choice every day.

Remember also, Fate is not some blind, illogical force that goes around impulsively bestowing its favours and punishments at random. Fate and Karma, is the outcome of personal, family, group, national, and racial events.

You are at liberty and have free will at all times. You can choose how you affect the lives of those around you. You can shape your own destiny, you can shape your present life, and you can shape your own future, by what you do and how you do it

*Excerpts and further reading from Bahram Elahi,
"The path of perfection," and "The guide book, a channelled teaching of our time."

(78)
Solomon's Reply To Mary

One day Mary asked Solomon, "How come my partner will not change?"

Mary had exhausted herself, her health and her bank balance in her attempts to change her partner and his behaviour. Solomon said, "Mary you and your partner met each other at a certain place and time. You both decided to form a relationship.

In the beginning all aspects of the relationship appeared normal. You were both relatively compatible with each other. You had similar interests, beliefs and conditioning. There were times when you neither questioned, nor doubted your own behaviours or that of your partner. At other times you realised that some of these behaviours were unacceptable and inappropriate.

Following a chain of events, which occurred in your life, it was necessary for you to attend for therapy. The therapy you received, plus your own inner knowing, brought you to a new level of awareness. What this actually meant was that you began to see life from a different perspective. You realised that some of your own past behaviours were unacceptable and some of the behaviours of your partner, family, and friends were also unacceptable and inappropriate.

Mary, one day in the recent past, you awakened to a different level of awareness. You began to see that there was a life outside the existence you perceived to be normal. You looked beyond yourself, beyond your relationship, beyond your conditioning. You saw a great expansive and exciting world out there. A world waiting to be embraced. A world of freedom. A world without conditioning or control. A world of fun and joy.

Your new awareness changed your perspective and beliefs. You started to look within yourself for answers. Answers to the reasons for your unhappiness, your loneliness, depression and addictive behaviours.

At this point you may also have realised, that your partner was not the person you thought he was, or would like him to be. You experienced hurt and rejection at his lack of support and lack of acceptance for the changes taking place within you. He suggested that you were "losing the plot," by becoming involved in all this "therapy business."

Because of his reaction to the changes you were making, and his inability to compromise, you both became more isolated from each other. The people who had been friends with both of you over the years had also started to drift away.

As time passed you became more attracted to like-minded people. You saw the employment you were now in, as unfulfilling. You started reading books and attending classes on personal growth and self-development, and eventually began training in different types of therapies. Your partner saw this as a rejection of him, and the particular interests, which were important to him. Changing to this new way of being was not an easy process. You felt lonely and isolated at times.

Then one day you had a "brain wave" – why not try and change your partner in the same way that you had changed yourself? You thought that if you could get *him* to see life as *you* now saw it, and see it from the same perspective as you, – then everything would be as you thought it should be. Your idea was to change *him* to the kind of person *you* thought he could be, and more importantly the kind of person you thought he *should* be. If you could change him to be more like you, life could be more harmonious and happy for both of you, – or so you thought.

To give you some insight into how you were attempting to change your partner, I Solomon will tell you a story:

When you first formed a relationship with your partner, you both wore similar shoes. The same brand, colour, and make. Because you had something in common, you were both attracted to each other. The only thing that was different was the size of the shoes, and the feet that were in the shoes, (you both had similar behaviour patterns, attitudes, and similar belief systems). You were not totally at ease with your shoes the first day you tried them on, (you were not totally comfortable with your own behaviour or the behaviour of your partner on your first date). You felt there could be something better, more suitable for you somewhere "out there," – (someone you could be more compatible with). But since there were no other obvious or major choices available at the time, you decided to buy these shoes and hold on to them, (hold on to old belief systems, old ways of being and hold on to this person).

As time progressed you found your own shoes were less and less compatible with your feet, (your own behaviours and belief systems were less and less acceptable to you, and those around you).

As your awareness changed you made a decision to let go of these shoes and not to purchase this brand or make of shoes again, (you made a decision to change your attitude and your belief systems and discontinue with the behaviours that were affecting yourself and others.

Over a period of time you became aware that there were other shoes available to you, different brands, makes, and colours, (a new and healthier way of being, a new awareness, new belief systems).

You decide to purchase a pair of these new shoes. You are absolutely delighted with them, (delighted with this new you). You tell everybody about these new shoes, (this new awareness), and how they too can acquire a pair for themselves if they wish. (You tell them, where they can also go to get help, to sort out *their* problems, and change *their* way of being).

What about your partner? He is still wearing the original shoes, which are the same make as the ones you used to own. (He is still behaving as he has always done, aggressive, abusive, manipulative and arrogant). He is quite happy and content in *his* shoes, and sees no reason to change them. (He sees nothing wrong with his behaviour or *his* belief systems).

One day *you* decide, it is time for *him* to change his shoes, (you decide it is time for him to change his ways, and change his behaviour).

What did you do?

Did you march up to your partner with your new realisation, and say to him, "Take off those shoes, they are no longer appropriate, (change your behaviour). You can't wear those shoes anymore, they are not healthy for your feet, (you can't live as you have been living anymore). Change to a different pair of shoes, (change your way of living, and become a different person). Those shoes will damage your feet, (you and your behaviour will damage your health). You must buy a new pair like the ones I have just bought, (you must change your ways, have a new awareness, –BE LIKE ME)?"

What you are implying here is that the way your partner is living his life is wrong, and that the way *you* are now living your life is right.

Why should he change his shoes, (his ways) just because you say so, or because you found change and awareness a joyful and happy experience?

You may be trying to prevent him from getting hurt, and delayed on his journey, – but *his* feet are not *your* feet. *His* journey is not *your* journey.

Your partner may now be looking at you in utter amazement at what you are suggesting. He may be quite comfortable in those shoes, or he may be oblivious to any pain, or he may have blocked out and covered up the pain over the years, with plasters and painkillers. (Plastered over his pain).

Remember, originally you both wore similar shoes, the same brand and make, (originally you were compatible with similar beliefs and conditioning). But those shoes were on different feet, (your partner's experiences and learnings were totally different from yours).

Your partner may be working with the only reality he

knows. If his reality is pain and discomfort, he will seek and find pain and discomfort. If his reality is abuse he will be attracted towards people who are abusive towards him. He may be working with many different realities, without you being aware of it The shoes he is wearing could be the same make as the shoes that you once owned, but the feet in them are not the same as your feet.

Everyone's reaction to the same or similar situations or events is totally different. Your perception and awareness about particular events or possibilities apply only to you. You can share your experience, but don't expect someone else to change because of *your* experiences.

This person may have blocked their pain to such a degree that as far as they are concerned the pain does not exist. It may not be the time for them to heal and deal with their issues or wounds. They may not deal with these issues in this lifetime.

Who are you to decide, to what degree or speed someone should change or recover? How would you like to be forced to heal faster than you are able, in order to satisfy someone else's needs or belief system?"

"Mary, if you want a life of running, skipping, and jumping, a partner with a broken leg may not be compatible with you. If you want to experience the joys and excitement of life, a partner who is crippled with pain (whether this is physical, emotional or mental), may not be a suitable partner for you either. You cannot force someone to live or see life as you do."

"You may need to learn to let go of this person.

Allow them to be, and stay where they are at.

Allow them their own learnings.

They will be more compatible with a like-minded soul.

Allow them to move at the pace best suited to them.

Give yourself permission to have freedom. (Freedom for you is not necessarily freedom for someone else.

There was a time when conditioning was all you knew. (You only knew one way of being). You can bring awareness to someone of what you know, but you cannot force him or her to change to facilitate your belief systems or your new awareness.

Give yourself permission to move on with your life and your new awareness. Allow yourself to see and enjoy the new pastures and green fields that are available to you.

You will meet like-minded souls in a world of freedom, where you don't need to force or control."

Are *you* trying to force or encourage someone else to change because of *your* belief system or *your* experiences?

...Solomon

(79)
Intrusions On Your Mind

Are your thoughts constantly preoccupied with a particular person, event, or issue?

Are these thoughts driving your mind and body into a state of exhaustion?

Are you in a constant state of anxiety, because your mind is totally preoccupied by a particular person and what they have done, have not done, or may do? Is your mind constantly asking when, where, how, why, will he, will she, if, if he, if she, etc. etc?

What happens if your every waking moment is preoccupied with thoughts of this person? (This person could be in spirit or still living).

This could be a person whom you once loved, or who once loved you. You may still love or care about this person. The relationship you had with this person may be over for some time, and they have moved on with their lives and entered a new relationship.

Your thoughts could now be about how this person has hurt you, abused you, angered, shamed, or annoyed you, broken your boundaries, broken your trust, manipulated or controlled you, rejected or abandoned you. You may also have played a part in these behaviours with this person.

Are you allowing thoughts about this person to control your daily life, your every waking and sleeping moments? Are you allowing them to occupy your thoughts as you go about your day? Are they occupying your thoughts when you eat, when you work, when you socialise, when you exercise, when you relax, but most of all when you try to sleep? Do you spend endless hours talking to other people about this person?

Even as you sleep, are you dreaming about this person? Have hours, days, months, and sometimes years passed by, practically unnoticed by you, because you are so preoccupied by this person? Is your life on hold or passing you by, because of your preoccupation with this person? Are you allowing them and their behaviour to control your entire life?

Are a lot of those thought patterns going around and around in your head? "If only he/she, if only they did, said?" "If only they did not do that?" "Did they ever really love me?" "Who are they with now?" "Will they phone me today?" "If I had done what they wanted, would they have stayed with me?" "Will they come back?" "Should I ring them?" "How do they feel about me now?" "What has this other person (who they are with now) got, – that I don't?" In the physical sense, every time your phone rings, does your heart 'miss a beat'? Every time you see a car that resembles the same make or colour as theirs, – do you gaze intently at the driver, hoping to see if it is him/her?

How many more incidences bring back memories, (not necessarily all good memories), of the time you spent with this person? (The only way to decrease or release anxiety is to take action).

It may be time for you TO STOP! – STOP entertaining this person in your head, and STOP them occupying your mind to the point, where there is no room for thoughts about anyone or anything else. You need to create limits on the time you allow this person to occupy your life, otherwise you will become totally exhausted and may possibly become quite ill.

At this stage you may not only be allowing this person to affect your life, but you may be allowing them to control it as well.

In the physical world, imagine if every morning when you got out of bed, you found this person sitting at your breakfast table. As you sit into the car/bus to get to work he/she is there sitting beside you. As you go through your daily work he/she is standing or sitting beside you all day. As you travel home from work or elsewhere, he/she is there beside you again.

As you sit watching your favourite TV programme he/she is sitting there, interrupting, distracting, and chattering away in your ear. When you get into bed at night, he/she is also there. As you try to sleep he/she keeps chattering away to you.

How long would you allow this behaviour to continue? Is there a point when you would tell them to go, and leave your space, leave you in peace, and wait until they are invited to join you?

Who is allowing them to bombard your mental space with their presence? – YOU ARE!

At some point earlier on in this scenario, you may have felt this invasion of your space was TOO MUCH! But, you allowed it to continue, – until now, when it has become almost unbearable.

How do you stop your mind from entertaining this person? Do you want to stop? Is it habit or is it an inability to "let go," that allows you to continue doing what it is you are doing? Ask yourself, "Is it healthy for you, body, mind, and spirit, to allow this behaviour to continue?

YOU CAN STOP YOUR MIND from entertaining this person. It is *your* mind, and *your* body. Only *you* can decide where, when, and how, you can stop this intrusion on your mind space.

If you want to stop this intrusion, you could try this exercise.

The next time you find yourself thinking about this person, take a deep breath, and as you exhale say, "STOP! – This is as far as you trespass on my space today. I am not entertaining any thoughts of you today." "I close the door on any thoughts of you." (Imagine yourself closing a door and this person remaining on the other side of it).

Five minutes later this person may be back in your thoughts again, – "How did he/she get in?" (Did you leave the door unlocked, or slightly ajar)?

The next time when you become aware that you are entertaining this person (in your head), repeat the first exercise, but this time, – LOCK THE DOOR!

You may find that this works for a while, but the thoughts keep banging and banging away in your head – (he/she is banging away at the door).

You may be back in control of your head space again for a while, but their insistence on getting in, may eventually begin to wear you down. Ask yourself, " What can you do now?"

The struggle to keep this person out can be quite exhausting initially. While continuing to keep control of your own space, you can at this point in time (if you so wish) allocate them some time and space of your own choosing. You can say, "I will allow you half an hour this evening, between seven and seven thirty, (or whatever time you yourself choose, day or night), and once this time is up, – you are out." "I will then decide, if and when I might entertain you again."

Each time he/she enters your head before the time you have allocated them say, "Sorry, I am not entertaining you until the prearranged time."

Try not to allow your defences to fail you. You will find that this exercise will eventually free you up for the entire day and night, because *you* are back in control of your own time and space.

Once the prearranged time has arrived, you need to honour your commitment:

- Set your clock for the half hour or whatever time you have allowed.
- Light a candle.
- Sit down as if you were preparing for a guest to arrive.
- See this person arriving for the visit.
- Try to avoid getting into their space (i.e. imagining what they have been doing since you parted, or how they are

feeling about you at this moment in time).

- Try to stay in your own space with your own feelings.
- Allow every thought, feeling and emotion associated with this person to surface and come to the fore.
- Give yourself permission to have these feelings.
- Say out loud or to yourself how you are feeling at the moment.
- Allow yourself to feel whatever feelings you have, in relation to what has happened.
- Give yourself permission to cry if you feel like crying.
- Try not to blame, – blaming insinuates the other person is doing or has done something wrong. Blaming can render you powerless. You are powerless over what this person has or has not done, but you are never powerless over yourself.
- Try not to get caught up in "ifs." – "If he/she did." "If I did." "What if?"
- Try not to take their issues on board. Try not to make excuses for your behaviour or theirs, what has happened, has happened, there are no "ifs."
- Try and separate the person from the behaviour. You are not a bad person. He/she may not be a bad person either. – It may be *their behaviour* that you have difficulty dealing and coming to terms with.

Immediately when the allocated time is up, – stand up and say, "Your time is up, –You must go now!" "I will allocate a time in the future, when and if it is convenient for me to entertain you again. But until that time, this is *my* space, *my* time, and I will not waste endless hours, engaging in useless mind games with you or anybody else."

Your time and space has become your own once again. You now have the time and space to engage in healthy, happy, and productive thoughts and behaviours.

You may find it necessary to repeat these exercises on a regular basis, or until you reach a stage when weeks, and even months will have passed before thoughts of this person will enter your mind.

Affirmation:

I am in control of my own body, mind and spirit.

I will not allow anyone to intrude on my body, mind, or spirit.

(80)
Depression / Happiness

Depression is a feeling of helplessness and hopelessness.

You are helpless and hopeless over everyone and everything but you are never helpless or hopeless over yourself.

Even in the darkest moment, there is light.

Today ask yourself, what do you really want out of life?

What gives you the most happiness in life?

Do you enjoy the work you do?

Do you enjoy your place of employment?

Do you enjoy the people you work with?

Do you feel you would be happier in some other occupation or in different working conditions with different people who you could better relate to?

Do you prefer to work outside or inside?

What allows you to continue working and living as you are doing, if you are not happy? Is it conditioning perhaps that says, "Don't move." "Don't change." "Don't rock the boat?" Is it the insecurity that you may not get as good a job, with as good a wage again?

Are you working inside a building, looking at blank walls, with artificial lighting, with people who themselves are feeling dull and depressed? Are you sitting down most of the day when you would prefer to be active?

Would you prefer a job outside in the fresh air and sunshine, enjoying the country views and scenery, and the sounds of nature? Are you a child of nature and are out of harmony when you are inside concrete buildings? It may not be feasible for you to leave or change your job at the moment, – but you could use the money and resources available to you, from the work you are doing, to make life more enjoyable and happy. You could take up a sport or activity, which allows you to be outside in the fresh air.

You could start a weekend or evening course that allows you to be outside i.e. gardening, bee keeping, sailing, fishing, coaching outdoor sports, which long-term you could turn into a profitable full-time business. By doing this, you are seeing the job you are in as a means and source of providing you with what you really want and enjoy. You can negate any negativity you are feeling around your present job, by seeing the rewards you are reaping as a result of this job.

You also could be the person who would prefer to be using your skills and creating your dreams inside rather than outside. You could be a great musician and singer and would love to record your own album of songs, but currently find yourself making your living as a carpenter. You may not like working outside in the cold and wet, and have no interest in nature whatsoever.

You can still use this employment to fulfil your dreams. It may not be financially viable to suddenly quit your full-time job, but you could use some of your money, to have your voice professionally trained, and then maybe decide to record your own album. Someone somewhere may hear your songs and offer you a recording deal, which may give you the opportunity to work in the music business fulltime.

You could be a housewife whose children have now grown up and moved on with their own lives. This could be *your* time to fulfil that dream you have always had, – to write your own book or play, or to work in the publishing industry, media, radio or television.

Are you a commercial traveller, building up a business for your employer, travelling many hundreds of miles each week, and dreaming about starting your own business? – If you can do it for someone else, you can do it for yourself.

Are you in a dead-end job with no future prospects or opportunities for advancement? Are you feeling depressed and bogged down? You could use some of the money from this job to train for a job you would really like. There is a job waiting for you, which you would enjoy. It would give you everything you dream about, with steady employment, lots of opportunities for advancement and progression on a ladder of success.

There are many opportunities waiting for you to create your ultimate dream.

You must first of all believe this and believe in yourself. Everyone has an opportunity to be a success. Success is not all about the money you make. It's about how you enjoy making it and enjoy spending it, but most importantly how you enjoy life and living.

What do you want out of life? What would you enjoy? Dream it. Think about it. Write it down. Describe it in every detail in a written plan of action. What is it you would prefer to be doing with your life? Find out today who is doing what you would like to be doing. How did they get started? Make some phone calls. Write some letters to assimilate all the necessary information you will need, to apply for this type of work. You may need to attend some courses. Contact career guidance officers. Contact schools for adult education classes. Look up directories. Ask your friends or relations for advice, or what contacts they might have in your area of interest.

There are opportunities waiting for you and for everyone, but you will only find them when you decide what it is you want to do and then go searching. Follow up on all the leads and directions you get, no matter from where or from whom. Once you make the decision to move from what you are doing right now, to what you would prefer to be doing in the future, – that is the first and most important step. Next plan it out, draw it out on paper, create a blueprint, see it in your mind's eye, and start researching straight away.

Be awake, be grounded and be aware of everything you see, hear, and do.

Be ready when the postman calls, if you are not there to receive the letter, (that message of direction) the first or second time he calls, he may not call again for some time. This means if you are not ready and waiting, after you have asked for a sign or direction from your guides, angels, or God, and the information you have requested is delivered, it may be some time before this message will be sent to you again. You can receive this message via a sign you notice along the road. It could be a newspaper heading, article, or advertisement. It could come as information via your radio or television. It might come as a leaflet someone gives you or drops through your letterbox. Or, someone might just say something to you that will set your mind thinking. Life knocks on your door with opportunities many times a day. Be ready and waiting when opportunity knocks.

What is meant for you in this lifetime will not pass you by. The chance you have been waiting for may come like a bolt of lightening "out of the blue." And you will be amazed at how easy it was when you look back afterwards, as you are enjoying your newfound success and happiness.

You can make the first move. You can knock on the door of life and announce that you want a change in your life, whatever that change might be.

Instructions on using the divination chart at the back of this book

Place the chart that is enclosed at the back of the book flat upon a table, or alternatively, you can make a photocopy of the chart and if you wish, enlarge it for your own convenience.

Close your eyes, and slowly take a few deep breaths. Allow yourself to relax. Connect with your inner-self and the Divine Realm. You may be using the chart to ask for general guidance or you may have a particular question in mind. If you have a particular question, then focus your mind on that question.

There may be one relevant question for you today. You may be at a crossroads with regard to some decision you are trying to make or a question you would like answered.

There are eighty randomly numbered squares. Each number represents a specific story in the book. You can use a small coin or some small object of your choosing. The smaller it is the better, so that you can identify more accurately which of the numbers it seems to favour when it lands. If it falls outside the chart, simply drop it again until it lands within the outline of the chart. Hold the object about 20 centimeters above the center of the chart, close your eyes, and drop the object onto the chart. If it lands equally between two squares, this means that you must read the two relevant stories to more fully understand the answer to your question. If it drops on a corner between four squares, and you are unsure which number to pick, you can pick the number which is closest to the dropped object, or the number you feel is most relevant to you, or start the process once again.

When you drop the coin or small object onto the chart it will disclose which one of the eighty stories pertain to your question or concern. As you read the relevant story, ask your guides, angels, or God to provide you with the inspiration necessary to understand the wisdom of the message for you.

It may be necessary for you to read the story a number of times in order to fully comprehend its inner meanings, or you may only need just one line from one passage to inform or inspire you.

The chart can be used as a tool for self-reflection and the chapters, stories, and channeled words of wisdom can be used to help you accept your daily struggles, as spiritual challenges, and learnings. You can gain a new awareness of ways to meet life's challenges, with better insights and understandings. This can help you to resolve problems, develop inner-trust and self-belief. This will allow you to choose new and exciting directions and help you to have more of an understanding of what is happening for you in your life.

You can also use this chart in other ways. Close your eyes, and turn the chart around and around a number of times until you are not sure which way it is faced. As you hold the question in your mind, ask your guides, angels, God for guidance. Place one finger on the chart and make a number of circles with your finger on the chart. When you feel ready, select a position on the chart with your finger. Open your eyes and read the number upon which your finger has rested. That is the number of the story to which you have been directed to read.

You can use a pendulum to dowse over the chart. Again, close your eyes; focus on the question or issue. Ask for guidance from the higher beings to be directed to the answers, which are for your greater good at this point in time. When you are relaxed and ready, open your eyes, allow the pendulum to move and dowse. Place your finger on each number, one at a time, as you dowse with the pendulum. If the answer to your question is yes, read that story, if the answer is no, move on to the next number and so on. You can also use the pendulum to give you a 'yes' or a 'no,' as you move your finger down the index, (at the front of the book), whilst keeping the question in your mind, ask the question; "Is this story applicable to me at this point in time?" Start with story one. If you get a "no," then move on to story two and ask the question again. If you get a "no," move on to three and four and so on, until you get a "yes." This is the story most relevant for you at this point in time.

You could also photocopy the divination chart, or cut out eighty equal squares of paper or cardboard and write the numbers on them 1-80. Then face the numbers face downwards. Turn them around and mix them up. Then with your eyes closed ask the divine power, God, or your higher conscience to direct you to pick the number most relevant to you today.

If you do not have a particular question in your mind, and would like general guidance in your life, ask your higher consciousness, God, guide, angels, that you may be directed to pick the story that is applicable to you and your life at this point in time.

If you have not used a pendulum before; there are many interesting and informative books available, including "The Pendulum Book," by Jack E. Chandu. "Pendulum Power," by Greg Neilsen and Joseph Polansky. "Pendulum" by Francis Hitching. "Anyone Can Dowse For Better Health," by Arthur Baeiley. And "Divining The Future," by Laura Scott and Mary Kay Linge.

Awaken that golden nugget within, the real You which is glowing brightly waiting to be discovered.

Divining Chart

29	2	17	77	3	25	18	61
71	33	26	19	12	5	41	34
52	60	13	66	49	14	35	28
21	42	36	57	1	43	39	9
74	15	58	65	38	51	44	37
30	23	16	73	6	59	27	45
8	62	24	31	67	20	53	7
46	32	75	68	11	54	47	40
76	69	22	55	48	10	70	63
56	78	4	64	79	72	80	50